The Origin of the Virus

First published in the UK September 2021

A catalogue record for this book is available from the British Library

ISBN: 978-1-85-457106-9

The Origin of the Virus

Published by:

Clinical Press Ltd.

Redland Green Farm, Redland, Bristol, BS6 7HF

With permission of the Italian publishers Chiare**lettere**.

The book *L'Origine del Virus* which this book is based on is available in Italian, Portuguese and Romanian.

The Origin of the Virus

The hidden truths behind the microbe that killed millions of people

Paolo Barnard

Dr. Steven Quay

Prof. Angus Dalgleish

Clinical Press Ltd.

L'Origine del Virus
Chiarelettere

Preface

In a disturbing reconstruction of events two of the most reputable scientists in the world reveal for the first time to the public the deadly biological secrets of the coronavirus that causes COVID-19. These were known to the Chinese authorities and to an elite of Wuhan scientists in the very early stages of the first Chinese epidemic, then were covered up under a layer of lies, omissions and obfuscations with later complicity of some people working for the chief US Public Health Agencies and even in scientific journals.

Prof Angus Dalgleish and Dr Steven Quay were coordinated by Italian reporter Paolo Barnard in a year long investigation.

SARS-CoV-2 was endowed with molecular features that made it unusually able to strike the human body way beyond what this class of viruses normally can do. That's why it kills and sickens so implacably. Its aggressive nature is ascribable to extreme laboratory experiments called Gain of Function, that manufacture novel deadly pathogens in Biosecurity facilities which, as historical records show, are often prone to accidental escapes like the one that gave origin to COVID-19.

Had the Chinese central authorities immediately alerted the international community and policymakers the world over of both the accidental leak and of the foreboding associated with the manufactured deadly features of SARS-CoV-2, very large numbers of lives could have been spared.

The authors of this chilling account of events surrounding the worst health crisis in a century firmly believe that unless these facts are further investigated and those responsible are called to account, it is highly likely the world is destined to re-live this catastrophe all over again and possibly much worse.

A Deadly Silence

by Paolo Barnard

Introduction

The real crime against global health committed in China, well before this pandemic became a world scourge, was the conspiracy of silence by both the authorities in Beijing and by an elite of Wuhan virologists to cover what they already knew of the extreme perils associated with the novel coronavirus that had just accidentally escaped one of their research facilities. In fact, they had very early knowledge – since at least January 2020 when Covid-19 was responsible for less than three thousand cases and no more than one hundred victims confined to Wuhan – that this virus had been endowed with lethal molecular features well beyond what is normally found in its class, which will be fully illustrated in this work later on. Had they immediately alerted the international health community, the media and policymakers the world over of both the leak and of the foreboding associated with those deadly features of SARS-CoV-2 no doctor in the world was aware of, very large numbers of lives could have been spared. They did nothing of the sort.

This book is a shocking account of the extreme experiments, of the repeated cover-ups and of the international collusions that led to the outbreak of the worst pandemic in a century. For the first time the public will be acquainted with what really lies at the heart of the nefarious molecular machinery that has now killed more than 4 million humans and disrupted life as we knew it on the entire planet.

Two among the most reputable living scientists, Prof Angus Dalgleish and Dr Steven Quay, have contributed their extensive knowledge and first hand research work to my journalistic quest, shining a disquieting light not just on the Chinese handling of the outbreak but also on those in the West that strived for the truth to be obscured, including some scientific journals. SARS-CoV-2, they reveal, bears beyond any possible doubt the hallmarks of the most extreme form of virological manipulation, called Gain of Function (GOF), which the Wuhan Institute of Virology (WIV) was practicing on a regular basis in cooperation with other so called Biosafety laboratories in China.

Between December 2019 and the beginning of 2020 the leading coronavirus expert at the WIV, Dr Zheng-Li Shi, was in all probability the first, or at any rate the most qualified scientist to sequence SARS-CoV-2 as contagion was taking hold in her own city. Among the host of amino acids in the Spike proteins – the protruding arms – of the novel coronavirus lay a number of *molecular weapons* that were known in the scientific literature for their potential to lead to extraordinary pathogenicity rampaging through many different classes of human cells. She knew that no other member of the SARS-CoV-2 family had ever been found to possess them and that Gain of Function experiments had in the past purposely inserted at least one of those weapons in the first 2003 SARS coronavirus. Zheng-Li Shi's vast experience in the field no doubt told her, in those fateful first days of the Chinese epidemic, that as the pathogen was now travelling the world through the intense connections Wuhan has with international hubs, it would almost certainly trigger a dreadful pandemic precisely because of the dangerous and highly unusual biological weaponry she was observing in its genome.

In the meantime the Chinese authorities were busy covering up all they could by having crucial evidence erased from databases or taken offline, and intimidating or arresting all those who were trying to alert the outside world of the realities on the ground in Wuhan. Even when the eminent virologist had an outstanding opportunity to notify international colleagues of what she knew by giving it prominence in her *Nature* paper of February

2020, in which she and colleagues described the sequence of SARS-CoV-2, Zheng-Li Shi made no mention of its dreadful molecular features.

To be fair, readers must realise that Zheng-Li Shi's mitigating circumstances lie in the fact the the entire Wuhan Institute of Virology had long been taken over by the Chinese Military, the PLA, as this book will later document. Also, since January 2020 Major General Chen Wei was charged by Beijing with supervising all COVID-19 operations precisely at the WIV, as publicly stated by the Chinese government controlled *The Global Times*. It is a fact that Zheng-Li Shi was never free to talk about what she knew.

Let us stress again that an *early disclosure* of the molecular weaponry may have allowed both the WHO but above all the unsuspecting governments and their more competent scientific advisers to enact far stricter and earlier counter measures to limit human contacts and to shut down most international travel when it really mattered, saving countless lives.

This book is, above all, about the use of compelling documentary, biological and factual evidence in unravelling a stomach clenching account of what allowed Covid-19 to engulf the world. It's not just that the coronavirus causing it did in fact escape from a Chinese lab and had nothing to do with a natural spillover from bats to humans. It is outrageous enough that whitewashing, partisan political interests and plain lying on a staggering scale – in China but also in some sections of the Western establishment – were allowed to conjure up in bestowing humanity with the worst health crisis in a century. The crucial question here is why, up until recently, most of the mainstream news media and scientific publications were de- facto complicit in this scandal?

The answer has to do almost entirely with Donald Trump. Before we continue, let us stress in the most unequivocal terms that far from taking a stand for or against the former US President, here we spell out facts, and just those.

So as it happened the most fundamental and urgent questions surrounding the emergence of the new pestilence were entirely hijacked, even muffled, by events taking place far away from China: 2020 was an election year in the United States, Donald Trump had long become one of the most internationally loathed figures in the history of contemporary politics, loathed by the Liberal media, by gender and minorities advocacy groups, by large sections of the financial powerhouses and Big Tech and by almost all academia. He had to be dethroned, period. On March 16th 2020, at 18:51 in Washington DC, the President tweeted the following: *"The United States will be powerfully supporting those industries, like Airlines and others, that are particularly affected by the Chinese Virus"*. It was pandemonium. The words *"Chinese Virus"* instantly supplied Trump's foes with the perfect Politically Correct ammunitions to pound his entire presidency as diplomatically irresponsible, racist, promoting the stigmatization of ethnic groups. That Tweet in particular was accused of having triggered a string of racially motivated hate crimes. When exactly one year later, on March 16th 2021, a white youth rampaged through a number of massage parlours in the city of Atlanta killing eight people among which were six Asian women, again the blame was squarely placed on the infamous Tweet as having inspired the crime. From that moment onwards anyone who dared to criticize China, particularly with reference to the science of the novel coronavirus, would instantly be chastised, then labelled as a Republican supporter, a racist, an obscurantist and suspected of working to grease the President's electoral machine. If Donald Trump had accused China of being the birthplace of Covid-19 then Chinese science must be innocent by default, team orders.

The scientific journals were no exception, particularly the influential *The Lancet*. As a consequence any scientist, no matter how reputable, who could not bring him/herself to believe that a virus could jump from bats to humans in such foggy circumstances and with no trace of any evolutionary path behind it, and who refused to rule out the lab-leak hypothesis would be stigmatized as a *"conspiracist"* or a *"crackpot scientist"*. His/her destiny was that of the pariah and he/she cold kiss goodbye to both research funding and a spot in any scientific publication. It would be left sixteen months later to the British Medical Journal to recite a mea culpa for that politically motivated and hysterical censorship of free enquiry within the research community. (1)

A month earlier Dr Filippa Lentzos, codirector of the Centre for Science and Security Studies at King's College, London, had confessed to the *Wall Street Journal* that *"Some of the scientists in this area very quickly closed ranks... There were people that did not talk about this, because they feared for their careers. They feared for their grants."* (2) It is not a mystery that as soon as strict partisan allegiance was no longer needed to topple Donald Trump following Joe Biden's ascent to the White House, as if by magic the lab leak hypothesis for SARS-CoV-2 was no longer taboo.

This is how hundreds of millions of citizens were denied access via the mainstream media to a balanced, objective and deliberative scientific debate on the true nature of the disease that has been ravaging their existence. Sadly, as a consequence, so many sceptics among the general public were left to the convulsions of conspiracy theories on the Web.

In the same fashion virtually all that we reveal in this book never found the outlet it deserved. From the scientific lies and criminal omissions by the Chinese health authorities to the cover-up organised by researchers in Wuhan and by their sponsors at the heart of US and UK research agencies and also the true picture of the biological deadly nature of SARS-CoV-2 --- all has been purposely obscured. Again, the overall human cost of all this has been horrendous.

With the outbreak of Covid-19 science smeared its own reputation for the 30 pieces of silver required to depose a politician and necessary to cover the tacks of its own *liaisons dangereuses* with extreme virology.

In so doing it brought back memories of the dark days of Galileo.

Now to the core of this exposé. I'll start with an account of the journey that led me from the mainstream narrative on the natural origin of SARS-CoV-2 to the discovery of a chilling reality.

The Secret Passageway behind the Old Bookcase. How this journey started.

"I was telling people, I know enough about HIV that if I wanted to I could probably get HIV to infect through the airborne route."

Professor Simon Wain-Hobson put it to me in this way, like a waiter suddenly dropping a whole stack of plates which crash onto the floor while he stands there staring at you, in this case through the screen on the other side of the Zoom call. He's one of the world's top retrovirologists, and his name carries a great deal of clout. He was a senior researcher at the Pasteur Institute in Paris, no less. I was interviewing him in March 2020 about Covd-19 [(3)] while in Europe it fell to Italy to be the first country ravaged by the new airborne virus.

I thereby realized in that moment that scientists today can manipulate a virus like HIV in order to transform it into a mass pathogen which is much easier to transmit than it naturally would be. But why would they do something like this? The genetic technique used to achieve this goal, Wain-Hobson would explain, is called "Gain of Function of concern", a branch of study of microorganisms unknown to most people, including the majority of doctors, politicians, and the mass media. Its rationale is described as the hypothesizing in laboratory experiments, and thereby anticipating, the most aggressive mutations of natural viruses, especially animal viruses that could spread to humans, with the aim of learning how to fight them before they arise, and consequently prevent hypothetical pandemics.

I didn't waste a second casting any doubt on what this eminent virologist had just affirmed; on the contrary, two things happened to me. The first was the mental image of someone who is unknowingly HIV-positive — the virus connected to AIDS — taking a plane from Rome to Milan and, in just a few minutes, transmitting this tragic illness to ten, twenty, or even more people, simply by talking or laughing, maybe by coughing a few times, while on board, at the check-in desk, in line, on the shuttle to the terminal, then in a taxi and finally back in the flow of normal life. It is horrifying to imagine AIDS being transmissible like the flu.

The second thing that I "saw" in front of me was what happens in certain black-and-white mystery films, when the protagonist accidentally discovers that by removing a book from a bookcase, it suddenly turns to reveal a secret passageway, which would lead to a tunnel, which would then lead to other passages and finally to a crucial place for the plot. This is exactly what happened in my mind after hearing Wain-Hobson's words, and the place to which my mind was led was Wuhan, China, in front of the Biosafety Level 4 lab where for years Chinese scientists had been conducting experiments on coronaviruses in bats in partnership with the Wuhan Center for Disease Control and Prevention.

As soon as my eyes could turn back to Prof Simon Wain-Hobson, the question was inevitable: *"Doctor, in Wuhan, China, in those labs which are now well-known throughout the world, were they manipulating coronaviruses?"* Calmly, he replied: *"China is working on influenza and coronavirus Gain of Function."* Immediately, I asked: *"So one of the hypotheses on the origins of this coronavirus would be that it was manipulated in that laboratory or somewhere else in China* (or even somewhere else in the world). *Would that check out?*" He took a long pause, and already this told me that I hadn't said something stupid — a bad sign. Then he replied: "*[That question's a] difficult one because we don't know everything that was going on in that Wuhan lab. Everything I see about this virus shows that it's not an engineered virus... but it could've been a virus that was isolated and escaped, that's a possibility, indeed.*"

This exchange would fling open the doors to an unthinkable world, one that is also, to a certain extent, disturbing, as I'll soon explain. I'd have to always keep clear in my mind that, on that day in March 2020, the person who was talking to me was without a doubt an authoritative academic disciple of the most rigorous molecular biology practiced anywhere in the world, under the auspices of a body like the Pasteur Institute in Paris. I wasn't chatting about conspiratorial fantasies with friends.

From the French capital, the road that would lead me to strengthen my suspicions that this could not be a natural virus takes me to the Liguria region in Italy.

As I already said, Italy in those weeks was the worst cemetery for Covid-19 in the world, and people were dying in the north of our country as nowhere else. In an email exchange I was participating in with Dr. Wayne A. Marasco, professor of Medicine and Immunology at Harvard University, and Giorgio Palù, Professor of Microbiology and Virology at the University of Padua, it was the latter who answered in a single dramatic line my question, "*Why are people dying like this only here?*" In fact, he wrote: "*In Lombardy, the rate of hospital admission of positive cases reaches 60% and this, like SARS-CoV-1, is a nosocomial spreader. Big mistake.*" (4) Of course, it is plausible that cramming people into hospital wards while they are sick with an unknown contagious and even deadly illness might only make the situation worse, but this still couldn't explain how a flu-like respiratory illness would decimate people even while they were receiving modern intensive care treatment. This didn't explain how it could attack young and healthy people, and even doctors with immediate access to cutting edge care, to the extent that it even created throughout the world a new syndrome for young survivors of the virus with no preexisting conditions that gained the foreboding name of *Long Covid*. There was something anomalous in the pathogenicity of the new SARS-CoV-2, something sinister, and certainly not common in nature; in fact, some neurologist and neuroradiologist friends told me about studies looking into the possibility that this virus could cross the blood brain barrier and attack the brain.

The scientific journal *The Lancet* posed in the following manner the most nagging questions regarding those serious long-term effects in survivors: "*What are the diagnoses, definitions, and phenotypes of illness that are grouped under the term Long Covid? How long does it last? Who is at risk of serious or prolonged sequelae? What are the underlying causes and mechanisms? How do we prevent or reduce the effects of such sequelae on patient health and wellbeing? Are there any effective treatments to aid patient recovery and the regain of full function?*"[5] It was obvious that this virus made people sick in ways that were truly unusual in their diversity, so far as to leave modern medicine speechless. But, I wondered, how was this possible?

It was at this point that an anesthesiologist from Liguria, working in the Villa Scassi Hospital in Genoa, sent me a shocking video of what was happening. [6] The images captured by his cellphone (and then rejected by all of the mainstream media, both Italian and British) showed something very different from the familiar litany then in vogue about a disease that struck only the elderly and those who were already sick. There was a young man intubated in a state of emergency, nurses didn't even have time to remove his anorak, while his chest was pumping as if during a marathon. There were women whose average age was frighteningly low, and one could see exhausted patients packed together in the halls, other young people in wheelchairs strapped to IVs. This deep-throat anesthesiologist said to me on the phone, *"We're not understanding a thing. We pump oxygen but it doesn't reach the lungs. Someone will be breathing better, but then he'll have a terrible case of dysentery. And, most of all, we see tons of instances of venous thrombosis, ischemia, cardiopathy, and all of it overlapping..."* Tragic words, which found confirmation several weeks later in the publication EBioMedicine of *The Lancet* in an editorial with a title that remains unforgettable to me: *"The four horsemen of a viral Apocalypse: the pathogenesis of SARS-CoV-2 infection."* (7) It's worth taking the time to read a few lines from it.

"The pathogenesis of coronavirus disease 2019 (Covid-19) may be envisaged as the dynamic interaction between four vicious feedback loops chained or happening at once. These are the viral loop, the hyperinflammatory loop, the non-canonical renin-angiotensin system (RAS) axis loop, and the hypercoagulation loop... The viral feedback loop includes evading the host's innate response, uncontrolled viral replication, and turning on a hyperactive adaptative immune response. The inflammatory loop is composed of the exuberant inflammatory response feeding back until exploding in an actual cytokine storm. Downregulation of the ACE2/Ang-(1–7)/Mas1R axis leaves the lung without a critical defense mechanism and turns the scale to the inflammatory side of the RAS. The coagulation loop is a hypercoagulable state caused by the interplay between inflammation and coagulation in an endless feedback loop." (ibidem)

As if that weren't enough, the conclusions of the study painted an alarming picture of the gaps that modern medicine, despite its stunning points of specialization, had to admit in front of this new virus. "... *One of the main gaps is the dynamic interplay between the host and the virus and how to modify it to improve disease prognosis,"* (ibidem) it said; that is, it is completely unclear what truly happens between the body and the mechanisms of Covid-19. And even more disturbing, if one focused on the unknown origins of the virus, was the admission that "*... There is a big difference in transmissibility, which is highest for SARS-CoV-2, among β-coronaviruses despite similar structure and functioning."* (ibidem) Then, even closer to the point, the authors confessed that "*The Virus's mechanisms to invade other organs beyond the lung are already poorly known."* (ibidem) It was enough.

On May 5th, 2020 I contacted one of the world's top pathologists in order to ask him precisely this question: "*Covid-19 causes an unheard-of quantity of clinical ailments in some patients. I wanted to ask: is this a common phenomenon in other human viruses, or is this one in particular unusually multipathogenic?*" He is Prof David Walt from the Department of Pathology of Harvard Medical School, known as one of the pioneers of biological engineering. His response was even more unsettling than what I have written above on the strange pathogenicity of SARS-CoV-2:

"*I really don't know. I think it is pretty unusual.*" [8] Unusual...

Three words echoed in my mind "*Gain-of-Function*" connected to the anomaly of a Betacoronavirus that suddenly breaks with its family genetic tradition to become a mean pathogen. Isn't this what happens in those labs where extreme virology is practiced?

The last ring in the chain that tied me to the certainty that the Covid-19 pandemic had not simply sprung out of a natural process — to which would then be added many other pieces of scientific evidence— was a passage I found while I was racking my brains over the latest torrent of molecular biology, by which I mean the latest piece of scientific research that I needed to read in order to orient myself in the infernal complexity of SARS-CoV-2. It presented itself to me, clear and simple, in the following terms: "*Unique to coronaviruses, the 3' to 5' exonuclease activity of nonstructural protein 14 (Nsp14) confers proofreading, thereby enhancing genomic replication fidelity. Unlike other RNA viruses that undergo error-prone replication, coronaviruses use Nsp14 exonuclease, which is the first identified proofreading enzyme encoded by an RNA virus and is likely an adaptation to accommodate the large RNA genomes of coronaviruses. This proofreading function implies that coronaviruses mutate at a less frequent rate than other RNA viruses."* [9] I'll simplify: when RNA viruses replicate themselves, they split their genetic code, exactly as human cells do with their DNA. But, unlike these, which usually split perfectly, RNA viruses make errors that potentially cause their twins to contain mutations, which in the majority of cases are defects that end up weakening them, but can also be mutations that make them more aggressive. Coronaviruses, meanwhile, have a mechanism (called Nsp14) that ensures that they make fewer errors, meaning they replicate rather accurately and mutate more slowly.

Now, logically this would mean two things that apparently contradict each other: the first is that SARS-CoV-2, in changing less frequently than other viruses, theoretically is less likely to develop "malign" mutations that would make it resistant to treatment; but, on the other hand, it is also less likely to weaken itself on its own over time, thereby knocking itself out of the picture.

It's precisely this last feature that makes it the ideal candidate for a successful Gain of Function experiment: a stable virus that shoots itself in the foot much less than other viruses do, but which will nevertheless be forced through a barrage of mutations by the scientist's hand in order to achieve the malignant one that will result in efficient infection of human target cells. Thus the relevant scientific publications and accolades. That is, barring any bumps along the way…

But up to that point, I had been navigating through suppositions that were, nonetheless, beginning to paint an unstable picture. It was time to put my ideas in order.

First point: there are laboratory techniques known as viral Gain of Function by which geneticists or molecular biologists can select any given virus — be it one from animals or humans, be it more or less infectious or pathogenic — and manipulate it, giving it new qualities. In extreme cases, they might even make it more virulent, even lethal, pandemic, and this is Gain of Function of concern.

Second point: precisely in Wuhan, in the high-security laboratory referred to as Biosafety Level 4 (but also in far less secure settings), multiple coronaviruses originating in bats had been isolated, and in some cases, they were manipulated through Gain of Function. This had been happening for a long time, as this book will detail later.

Third point: today the planet is in the grip of a new coronavirus, the cause of Covid-19, which attacks the human body in perhaps never-before-seen ways for a microorganism of that category. Furthermore, these coronaviruses have replication systems that make them more stable and less given to weakening themselves over time, making them, in theory, ideal subjects of experimentation in laboratories, which are notoriously prone to accidental escapes.

It was then, just in the first few weeks of the disaster, that the idea of the *unnatural* quality of this virus became steadfast for me. In other words, I wondered: these abstruse terms *zoonotic diseases* and *zoonotic origin*, which we had all learned by dint of hearing them used far and wide in explanations of how a virus from bats could have latched onto another animal, the so-called intermediate host species, and then from there, bizarrely, onto humans, by means of a cut of meat prepared or consumed in Wuhan… in short, this zoonotic theory, I wondered, does it really seem as realistic as the mainstream media insists on repeating it is, despite the absence of definitive evidence? It was a question, I'd find out, that a substantial number of esteemed names in international research were already asking, specifically in relation to the numerous plausible scientific hypotheses on the unnatural origin of Covid-19.

Unearthing Viral Gain of Function.

I needed to dig; however, I was bumping up against layers of fear and reticence precisely in those dissident scientists, one of whom, an eminent American microbiologist, confessed openly: *"Writing is formal...and thus dissent in writing is career-threatening"*. [10] He declined my offer to have his name connected to this book. But I kept digging. Just as the teams of Dr. Kirsty Duncan and of Dr. Jefferey Taubenberger had done in the permafrost of the Spitzbergen Island in Norway and in the Alaskan tundra, when on behalf of the National Institutes of Health of the United States they unearthed from 1996 to 1998 several bodies that had remained frozen there for eighty years, eventually resuscitating a sample of the apocalyptic Spanish flu — an astonishing resurrection. [11]

And yes, that too was a feat of evangelical memory carried out in the name of the already mentioned rationale at the heart of the research known as Gain of Function of concern, even if, I should specify, the work on the Spanish flu conducted by these two scientists didn't formally fall within that branch of virology. But I have to ask for a moment of your patience, and I'll come back to Spitzbergen and Alaska shortly.

Understanding both versions of viral *Gain of Function* (i.e. *of concern*, and not) is fundamental for fully understanding a part of the content of this book. In fact, one risks reacting incredulously throughout the following pages, because instinctively one thinks, *"lies," "conspiracy theories," "like they'd even be able to do something like that" "it could never happen."* And it's in this void of guiltless public ignorance that colossal geopolitical, diplomatic, commercial, and even academic interests thereby had no problem relegating whomever doubted the zoonotic origin of SARS-CoV-2 into the bin of conspiracy theorists, no matter how authoritative these dissidents might have been, thereby gagging what was the most important investigation of this millennium. Because, in the words of an eminent member of Stanford University's School of Medicine, Prof David Relman:

"To stop the next pandemic, we must unravel the origin of Covid-19." (12)

And the next pandemic, if we consider the possibility of accidental infection through the results of Gain of Function of concern research held today in the laboratories of at least three continents, could make Covid-19 seem like a nice memory.

Gain is used in the sense of *"attribution." Function* is *"capability"*. In its broadest meaning, this research is rather easy to understand: its starting point is the fact that in less 70 years since the discovery of the double-helix in DNA, science has acquired the extraordinary ability to manipulate the micro-structures of molecules, proteins, and cells in the search of advancements for human health, nutrition, technology and the environment, precisely through giving them new capabilities or functions. In virology, *Gain of Function* has gone in two directions: in a few cases, it manipulates viruses in order to adapt them for the benefit of humans; but certain critical — that is, concerning — cases, for which I'll give examples further ahead, involve extremely dangerous experiments that have divided the scientific community, experiments that are relevant to our inquiry. But this latter category has, in effect, taken the entire branch "hostage," to the point that today, with the words Gain of Function, almost all experts intend Gain of Function of concern.

I'll now turn back to the Spitzbergen island and Alaska, eighty years after the worst mass-contagion in history, which killed at least 50 million people, much more than the medieval plagues known as the Black Death, contrary to what many imagine. [13]

When it becomes truly a matter 'of concern'

The miners and laborers that came to the Spitzbergen Islands in 1918 in search of a living wage were, for the most part, Europeans who had just survived the carnage of the trenches of World War I, and it would be hard to imagine a fate much crueler than theirs. Along with canteens and a few pieces of bread or dried meat, someone brought with him — or rather, inside him — the two infernal letters H1N1 of the deadliest virus in human history, the Spanish flu. It laid waste to them. The bodies were buried hurriedly in mass graves two meters underground, a depth at which, in that location, reigns perennial ice. It's the same natural "freezer" that preserved the body of an Eskimo woman in Alaska, who had been killed the same year by the same flu. We can only imagine the amount of tense and fearful precaution with which, a century later, the above mentioned researchers Kirsty Duncan and Jeffery Taubenberger worked to have pieces of tissue extracted from those cadavers in an attempt to revive the extinct virus. None of them knew at the time whether that frozen microbe was still intact and potentially active. An accident, a microscopic error, the mishandling of a vial while pathologists bent, two meters underground, over those frozen remains, would have been enough for an accidental infection to move from the Spitzbergen Islands or from Alaska all the way to their laboratories in Bethesda, Maryland, and then the world could have been once again slaughtered by the 1918 H1N1, to which no one has immunity anymore.

But that was the right time to do it, seeing as a chemistry genius named Kary Mullis had a few years earlier invented an incredible technique called PCR (polymerase chain reaction, which is still used today for Covid-19 swab tests) that allows for the reconstruction of an entire genome—a viral one, in this case—even from small fragments of it. It's a bit like if it were possible to perfectly reconstruct a face starting with only a few cells from the nose, a few facial hairs, a tiny piece of the ear. And this is how in 2012, Taubenberger publishes, in a decidedly positive tone, the results of that "resurrection." The scientist was clear about the motives that were at the heart of that concerning study: *"It has provided important information about how to prevent and control future pandemics"*, he wrote. (14)

This is precisely the raison d'être of Gain of Function of concern, even if, I'll specify again, the work of Duncan and Taubenberger was not exactly research carried out with viral GOF.

Nonetheless, it was not lost on this scientist that what they were doing was essentially playing with dynamite on a global scale, if not worse, and in fact he added tersely: *"The milestone achievement of reconstructing an "extinct" pandemic virus raised a number of questions that had not been asked before. The most fundamental of these was whether it was necessary or wise to recreate by molecular means a naturally extinct virus that represented one of the deadliest infectious agents in human history... We argue that learning the most closely guarded secrets of our deadliest biological enemies is an essential means of protecting ourselves from future events of a similar nature... Reconstruction of the 1918 virus has already been unexpectedly rewarding. Unquestionably, even greater rewards lie ahead"*. (ibidem)

Unfortunately, to the point of being able *"to prevent and control future pandemics"*... now we know that what was *"lying ahead"* for us was Covid-19, a pandemic that found science and medicine utterly unprepared.

The bitter irony I just expressed was the last feeling that ran through the auditorium of international scientists gathered together in Malta on September 12, 2011 when Dr. Ron Fouchier, a virologist from the Erasmus Medical Centre in Rotterdam, Netherlands, announced that his laboratory had used Gain of Function of concern to, and I quote, *"mutate the hell out of"* the already deadly avian influenza H5N1 in order to make it capable of infecting ferrets through the air, and therefore potentially capable of infecting humans as well. (15)

To give an idea of the shock that these words inspired in the scientists who heard them that day, it should be specified that this avian virus had already killed 60% of all of those —and we're talking about men and women— who contracted it through animal fluids (16). The abovementioned Spanish Flu, which became the worst pandemic in history, in comparison killed from 2.5% to 10% of those infected, while Covid-19 has a case-fatality rate that on average oscillates between 1% and 3%, depending on the area. It's worth making the comparison. This was the unthinkable level of potential mass death that Fouchier announced that day, hurrying to justify his Gain of Function research with, again, the promise of learning how to prevent future pandemics by first encountering in a lab the worst mutations that the H5N1 could, in theory, acquire in nature.

I was thinking about all of this in the summer of 2020, the first to come after the explosion of the Covid-19 pandemic, while one night I was walking along a road in the hills with numerous bats twirling rapidly above my head. Damned animals, people will say. But in that moment, mixing what I knew about Gain of Function of concern and those nocturnal flying creatures, I remembered these words: "*Yes, there is a danger, but it's not arising from the viruses out there in the animals, it's arising from the labs of grossly ambitious people.*" They were uttered in 2014 by Lord May, ex-president of the British Royal Society and, before that, Chief Scientific Adviser to her Majesty's government. He then added, without mincing words: "*The work they are doing* (GOF of concern) *is absolutely crazy. The whole thing is exceedingly dangerous*". (17)

That night, once again, the bookcase rotated, then there was the secret passageway, then the tunnel, and there I was again at the Biosafety Level 4 laboratory in Wuhan.

The British scientist was not the only harsh critic of this extreme branch of virology, and over the years names from the highest scientific ranks spoke out along with him, such as Prof Richard Ebright, microbiologist at Rutgers University in the United States; or such as the above mentioned Prof Simon Wain-Hobson, retroviologist from Paris's Institute Pasteur; and finally, I'll cite the young, brilliant epidemiologist from Yale University, Dr. Alison Galvani, among many others.

Lord May intervened with those comments in 2014 because another "bomb" had just gone off in scientific journals, this time launched by Dr. Yoshihiro Kawaoka from the University of Wisconsin-Madison in the US. He and his team had searched in the various genomes of the avian flu for the most closely related to the Spanish flu, then they mixed them to obtain a nearly identical pathogen to the one from 1918. Regardless, seeing as it didn't infect the guinea pigs enough (sic), they bombarded it with mutations until finally they obtained a version that was potentially devastating for humans too, since it could be spread through airborne transmission. (ibidem) Reading the rationale with which Kawaoka justified that use of Gain of Function of concern is incredibly eye-opening. He wrote in the journal *Cell & Host Microbe* on June 11, 2014:

"Since avian species harbour a large influenza virus gene pool that may contain influenza viral segments encoding proteins with high homology to the 1918 viral proteins (designated as 1918 virus-like virus proteins), the possibility exists for a 1918 virus-like avian virus to emerge in the human population as a pandemic virus; however, the likelihood of such an event remains unknown. To assess the risk of emergence of pandemic influenza viruses reminiscent of the 1918 influenza virus, we examined the

properties of influenza viruses composed of avian influenza viral segments that encode proteins with high homology to the 1918 viral proteins (designated as 1918-like avian viruses), which we generated by using reverse genetics". [18]

In other words: purely in theory, there's the as-of-yet unknown possibility that a devastating pandemic virus could emerge in nature, killing millions of people as a result. But no one knows if such a virus will ever exist. Therefore, we scientists have created it, and now we're sure it exists. This is the rather bizarre logic behind Gain of Function of concern, written in black and white. And the scientist then took pains to specify that the virus similar to the 1918 flu that they created in a lab was "*more pathogenic in mammals than an authentic avian flu virus*". [ibidem]

Other virologists modified a virus in ostriches labelled H7N1 and tried to make it pandemic in ferrets, with the goal of rendering airborne transmission possible from one human to the next. [19] We know that H7N1 has for us a mortality rate superior to that of the Spanish Flu by at least 30%. A team of German and Swiss researchers, in March 2013, had "tweaked" canine distemper to make it attack human cells. [20]

Finally, the already cited Ron Fouchier had created his monstrous Gain of Function of concern virus, that is, the mutated H5N1, in the middle of densely-populated areas in Rotterdam, and one can only imagine what could have happened — and still could happen — if someone accidentally became infected with a microbe that kills 60% of those who catch it in such a crowded place.

What fits this debate to a T is the revealing statement the above mentioned Dr. Marc Lipsitch of Harvard University sent me on the uncredited scientific benefits of this controversial field of research: "*In sum, Gain-of-Function research of concern has not been associated with major scientific advances to my knowledge, and is the target of debate.*"[21]

What Dr Quay, Prof Dalgleish and I would like to underline

clearly is that Gain of Function of concern is discussed here for another reason too, regardless of the origins of the current pandemic. It's this: to push for the reopening of the public debate on this scientific practice, just as Marc Lipsitch and Alison Galvani already pointed out in 2014: *"Given the risk of a global pandemic posed by such experiments, this risk assessment should be part of a broader international discussion involving multiple stakeholders and not dominated by those with interest in performing or funding such research."* (22) The level of risk which the Harvard professor is talking about relates precisely to the considerably concrete danger of one of these terrible pathogens accidentally escaping from labs. And we would not have written this book if the claim that Covid-19 did not take flight from a laboratory had any real basis in honest science.

The echo of Prof Simon Wain Hobson rang again in my ears at this point: *"China is working on influenza and coronavirus Gain of Function."* I will later on learn that in Wuhan some labs researching coronaviruses – namely the Wuhan Institute of Virology (WIV) and the Wuhan Center for Disease Control and Prevention – were in the habit of 'cooking' viral genomes as standard practice, there is no doubt about it, just as there's no doubt that some of these experiments were carried out in pretty unsafe laboratory settings.

Coronaviruses in all sorts of sauces, cooked in non-compliant kitchens.

The first to become world known was the SARS epidemic coronavirus which in 2003 sprang out of the Guangdong province in China. It was very aggressive but fortunately it subsided without infecting the entire planet. In 2004 at the WIV they started to mix genetic segments of SARS with other bits of coronaviruses in an attempt to infect human cells, just as one would mix ingredients for a new culinary recipe. In the project layout (partly financed by the US as I will later detail) the rationale for this kind of research was precisely the one at the foundation of Gain of Function work, namely to study the pandemic potential of coronaviruses by making them so in lab trials in order then to try and prevent future mass outbreaks. [23] From that moment onwards viral Gain of Function (including GOF of concern) accelerated at the WIV. The top researcher there, Dr Zheng-Li Shi, had been tutored, so to speak, by one of the most controversial Gain of Function of concern scientists in the world, namely Dr Ralph Baric of the University of North Carolina in the US, with whom she published a famous international study precisely on lab created *"chimera viruses"* starting with coronaviruses, which quickly demonstrated their pandemic potential on humans. In this case the genome manipulation technique was one of those that will leave no trace of the human hand. [24] In the following months researchers at the WIV made great strides in bats pathogens' Gain of Function and published their results in prestigious journals like the *Journal of Virology o Plos Pathogens.* [25]

This went on all the way till 2019 when the Covid-19 epidemic erupted in China only to become shortly afterwards an international catastrophe. But still the WIV kept on "cooking" coronaviruses as proven by the specifics of an allocation of funds earmarked National Institutes of Health (USA) to the Chinese on the 24th of July 2019. [26] It goes without saying that this kind of work must always be carried out in Biosafety Level 3 or Level 4 laboratories precisely because even the smallest of accidents can result in the mass killing of millions. Well, we now know for sure that Gain of Function "cooks" in Wuhan were sometimes working under substandard safety conditions in Biosafety Level 2 labs or even less, which is the level of biosafety expected from a dental practice.

This was candidly admitted in less controversial times, 2016 that is, by the coronavirus "chef in chief" Dr Zheng-Li Shi in the prestigious *Journal of Virology* [27], but no one at the time paid any attention, least of all the World Health Organization. And up until the start of the pandemic even the Beijing government had no qualms in admitting that some of the labs at the WIV were dangerously non-compliant with the best safety standards. In fact in April 2020 *Voice of America* managed a scoop by publishing Chinese State documents dating before the Covid-19 outbreak that unequivocally denounced those critical inadequacies. *Voice of America: "VOA has located state media reports showing that there were security incidents (at the WIV, author's note) flagged by national inspections as well as reported accidents that occurred when workers were trying to catch bats for study... About a year before the coronavirus outbreak, a security review conducted by a Chinese national team found the lab did not meet national standards in five categories... National reviewers found scientists were sloppy when they were handling bats."* [28]

The Maryland University (USA) expert in International and Security Studies, Dr Milton Leitenberg, who has carried out exceptional work on this subject, revealed to us in July 2020 that

"One of the researchers working at the Wuhan Center for Disease Control & Prevention described to China's state media that he was once attacked by bats, and he ended up getting bat blood on his skin... In another incident, the same researcher forgot to take protective measures, and the urine of a bat dripped "like rain onto the top of his head," reported China's Xinhua state news agent..." [29]

So it was a long acknowledged fact that the "scientific kitchens" at the Wuhan Institute of Virology, just like those at the Wuhan Center for Disease Control and Prevention, did not possess the best safety standards but still carried out extensive viral Gain of

Function experiments. This fact is of the utmost seriousness as it's an internationally established truism that no labs handling dangerous pathogens are 100% safe, even those at the top, and therefore to carry out Gain of Function work within settings where negligence in safety standards is commonplace borders on criminal folly. Unfortunately, there is no shortage of historical examples.

National Insecurity Labs

The most statistically plausible global catastrophes are the ones caused by human error, and not, as many believe, by human will. Nothing illustrates this axiom better than the senseless history of nuclear confrontation from the beginning of the Cold War to today. Only a few of the Earth's inhabitants realize they are alive thanks not merely to a single miracle, but to a whole list of miracles, when atomic annihilation was about to take place due to frantic misunderstandings and was just barely avoided. On October 27, 1962, at the height of the Cuban Missile Crisis, the US Navy intercepted two Soviet submarines, the B-59 and B-130, whose respective captains, Valentin Savitsky and Nikolai Shumkov, along with their crew, were not only exhausted but cut off from communications with Moscow. They were also unaware of the fact that the explosive charges which were being fired at them were only "cosmetic" and not an actual attack, meaning they were solely intended to force them to come to the surface and identify themselves. In those minutes brimming with tension, both Soviet captains lost their minds and shouted the order to arm the nuclear warheads they had on board. The last-second intervention of the second-in-command Vaili Arkhipov on the B-59, and the mental collapse of the person in charge of arming the missiles on the B-130, were all that separated humanity from nuclear World War III. (30)

But the point that interests us, due to its aptness in this book, is that both the veteran of the Soviet secret services Vladimir Orlov and the American naval historian Joseph Bouchard agreed that "*...the major danger was from an accident caused by the interaction of men and machines under the most trying of circumstances.*" [ibidem] Exactly what risked taking place in June 1999 during NATO's so-called "peace-support mission" in Kosovo, when a rash order given by an American general was ignored at the last second by a British commander, who told him, "*Sir, I'm not starting World War III for you.*" [31]

This is to say that more than a few times the lives of millions of people have been put at risk by completely human errors that arose in the context of technologies of mass destruction and were saved at the last second due to pure chance. And this is precisely what has happened, on no rare occasion, in laboratories where pandemic viruses are conserved or manipulated, particularly in virology research facilities categorized as Biosafety Level 3 or Level 4 like the one in Wuhan. Here too, only fortuitous occurrences have stopped global tragedies from taking place.

In 1978, the United Kingdom ran the risk of going down in history as the country that wasted nearly two centuries of fighting the tragic smallpox disease, which had finally been won thanks to global vaccination. At the Birmingham Medical School a laboratory photographer, Dr. Janet Parker, suddenly had violent dermatological symptoms that were then incomprehensibly underestimated. Only a few days before her death would Parker hear the doctors by her hospital bed whisper in disbelief the word "smallpox," the virus that kills one out of three people and had been identified for the last time and finally destroyed in Africa the previous year. How could it be that this pestilence had reappeared in modern Great Britain? The answer was so obvious that it was not immediately taken into consideration by the doctors looking after the young woman or by the WHO team that came to Birmingham in a heartbeat: Janet Parker worked in the lab of Dr. Henry Betson, where precisely smallpox was being studied. It had accidentally escaped, no doubt, and at the hands of professionals who were used to handling pandemic pathogens, despite the use of every possible technological precaution. The world of international scientists was in shock, and Dr. Betson took his own life before Janet died. Three hundred people were quarantined, and the whole world held its breath for the fourteen-day incubation period of a virus that had killed over 300 million people in the 20th century alone. Things went relatively well in the end. (32)

I've already cited the pandemic to end all pandemics, the Spanish flu, caused by the deadly H1N1 virus. In 1977 this monster, although mutated compared to the 1918 original, reappeared in Russia and in China. Some serious scientific researchers, who today at the height of Covid-19 would be labelled as "conspiracy theorists," suggested that it could only have escaped from a laboratory that was still preserving samples of a similar virus dating back to 1949, because the genome of the rediscovered H1N1 was missing decades of mutations, and therefore it had to be a sample that had remained frozen in a freezer for that entire duration of time. Here, once again, only chance stopped the evolutionary advance of that microbe toward worldwide carnage, because the consequent epidemic selected as its first victims young and very young people, who defeated it. The hypothesis that it had escaped from a lab was then backed up by a study published in 2010. (33)

Today no one knows exactly how to explain why the 2003 SARS virus didn't cause apocalyptic results, given its virulence, but above all its "habit" of escaping from leaky laboratories. This pathogen was inadvertently reintroduced among humans a full four times in China, always as a result of it escaping from the same laboratory (sic), and it managed to evade security measures once in Singapore and again in Taiwan. But what should be highlighted are the details about SARS escapes, because they seem too crazy to be true, and yet they are.

In August 2003 in Singapore a graduate student in virology, who actually had never even worked on this virus, became infected. It had been enough for the pathogen to be stored in a nearby freezer for it to mysteriously attack him, like the smell of fish that jumps out at you when you open the fridge in your home. [34] In Taiwan, the mess reached a scandalous degree: in December 2003, it was discovered that a well-known researcher invited to scientific congresses throughout Asia had handled infected liquids from a lab leak without even wearing a protective suit, a facemask, or gloves (sic), that is to say, bare-handed with his lab coat. And this was in front of other colleagues in the only research establishment with the label of Biosafety Level 4 in Taiwan, where the security measures should have been enforced with suffocating stringency. [35]

Now we come to the leaks of SARS in China. At the prestigious National Institute of Virology (NIV) in Beijing, in April 2004, a researcher was hit with serious respiratory symptoms and, in a considerably misty reconstruction of events, it seems that she had been free to go not once but twice to see her mother who was a doctor in Anhui Province, who was then infected with SARS and died. Alternatively, the WHO wrote that it was the mother who went to visit her daughter in the hospital in Beijing, but the general picture doesn't change: the virus infected the scientist at work and then was allowed to infect people on the outside. [36]

This leak of SARS would repeat itself, the same year, in three other cases and each time at the NIV, where it would later be uncovered that the source of the infections was a molecular study of the SARS virus that was believed to be inactivated but wasn't, and no one had checked the safety of this. Worse still: it was even handled in regular laboratories, and not in Biosafety labs, with a shocking degree of irresponsibility. [37]

And if a virus accidentally escapes from a laboratory and successfully infects a mammal 250 kilometres away by travelling through the air? Is it a fantasy? No. And if this virus ends up in a pond, then sticks to the wheels of a tractor wet with mud which will carry it into a farm, causing a massacre of animals? Fantasy? No. It's called Foot and Mouth Disease (FMD), it happened in the UK in 2007, and the economic damage it caused was enormous. (ibidem) But the point is this: we know that viruses can jump from animals to humans, so imagine if FMD, which escaped a lab in this sensational way, had adapted to infect us... infecting through the air at a distance of 250 kilometres. Is any comment necessary? Do we need anything else in order to believe that unthinkable human errors are common in laboratories? Maybe we do.

In the United States, microbes escaping from laboratories is almost a daily occurrence, at a rate of once every couple of days, even if they are usually less infectious pathogens, as reported in Select Agents and Toxins of the Centers for Disease Control (CDC). However, the risk is still there, and in fact the CDC cites an example from 2008 in which, despite all of the best precautions, a sterilizing autoclave exploded contaminating a lab worker with pathogen agents that were never revealed. [38]

The next year, the decontamination showers of a Biosafety Level 4 lab studying Ebola and smallpox malfunctioned, with the doors randomly opening to the general panic of the researchers. The news was reported in *USA Today* with the headline, *"Newly disclosed CDC biolab failures 'like a screenplay for a disaster movie'"*. [39] In 2011, a lab researcher studying the avian influenza, after noting that the decontamination shower wasn't working, took off her biosafety protective gear and simply walked out into the world. Miraculously, she was stopped and brought back inside. [40]

But it was the summer of 2014 that seemed to be marked as the most cursed year for pathogen leaks from American laboratories.

It was July when the Department of Health and Human Services closed its research centres on flu and anthrax at the Centers for Disease Control in Atlanta. Incredibly, around 60-70 workers had been exposed to anthrax while handling this lethal bacterium, convinced that it had been inactivated, but it wasn't. Only the immediate administering of antibiotics and vaccines avoided fatalities. Then it was revealed that another CDC laboratory had accidentally contaminated a benign strain of the flu called H9N2 with the instead deadly H5N1 avian virus, the very one that kills 60% of those who contract it. Here too fortuitous chance led to this discovery.

Finally, once again that year, in a warehouse of the National Institutes of Health close to Washington a lab employee stumbled upon sixteen old vials dated 1954. One of these broke while it was being handled by non-expert personnel. Luck would have it that a researcher took the trouble of analysing them before they were thrown away: some of them contained perfectly active smallpox, the pandemic killer. The principle of chance in Russian roulette saw that the one that shattered into pieces was not one of the vials containing the disease. (41)

However, at his point, before returning to the laboratories in Wuhan, to Beijing or elsewhere in Asia in an analysis of the true background story of Covid-19, one should ask how what I've described above translates into a concrete percentage of risk for citizens such as us. We are people who — at least until the fateful January of 2020 when we heard the name Coronavirus uttered for the first time — due to innocent ignorance worry about everything in life, from all things from debts to serious disease to our houses, more than we worry about being exterminated by something that could happen in that anonymous and obscure cement building in the urban outskirts which we never knew what it was, and it's actually a Biosafety Level 3 or Level 4 virology research facility.

But where are they?

One hundred and twenty six million human beings don't know today that they are living in close range of a Biosafety Level 4 virology laboratory, the ones where the most dangerous pathogens on the planet are handled, such as Ebola, smallpox and H5N1 avian flu. The area that's the most at risk? Europe, by far. This fact was revealed, long before the world's spotlight was pointed at Wuhan, by a group study led by the Department of Ecology and Evolutionary Biology at Princeton University (USA) which prophetically was already asking:

"Can the multiplication of the number of laboratories and their installation in densely populated areas cause a substantial increase in the risk of a mantriggered epidemic or pandemic? The results presented in this paper indicate that this may indeed be the case." (42)

The scientists pinpointed over 52 facilities of this kind in the world, a large portion of which were located right in the middle of places like Berlin, Hamburg, Rotterdam, Milan and Rome in Italy, Geneva, London, Prague, Bhopal and Pune in India (7.5 million inhabitants) Atlanta and Bethesda in the US, Taiwan, Singapore, Wuhan, around which enormous numbers of people live, work and, most of all, travel, both locally and from across the world. (ibidem)

One of the conclusions of the study, which we consider of essential interest for this book, states: "*The current situation, whereby new BSL-4 facilities tend to be located in regions of high population density, may ultimately result in the risks of an artificial outbreak occurring outweighing the risk of a naturally-arising global pandemic*". (ibidem)

And for the third time, after the secret passageway and the tunnels, my mind emerged on the other side in Wuhan, China, December 2019.

It is now necessary to cover one last stretch in order to master the full picture of scandals, omissions, lies and obfuscated genomic realities in Covid-19's history. Possibly some readers will have by now already pondered why when it came to the origins of SARS-CoV-2 the conundrum could not be simply and quickly solved by searching for traces of scientists' "cut and paste" work in its genome. Surely human manipulations leave an unmistakable signature, don't they? Well, here are the facts.

Manipulations Without Any Identity Card

The experts are widely divided on whether the manipulation of a viral genome is always recognizable after the act, or whether, on the contrary, the researcher's hand can avoid leaving any trace of itself. For example: Prof Simon Wain-Hobson, retrovirologist from the Pasteur Institute in Paris, was categorical on this subject with me: *"Making chimeras leaves a signature, and a bloody big signature."* (although it's been reported that recently he partly changed his mind) (43)

The scientific journal *Nature Medicine* published in early 2021 an editorial by Dr. Angela Rasmussen, who is affiliated with Georgetown University in the US, in which this expert virologist didn't even consider the question, dismissing it a priori as an example of "*... outright ridiculous conspiracy theories that spread faster than the virus itself.*" (44) In contrast, the equally authoritative Prof Richard Ebright, microbiologist at Rutgers University, directly responded in the following terms: "*WIV constructed a series of novel chimeric viruses encoding different receptor binding domains—with different receptor binding affinities—in an otherwise constant genomic context. And did so using "seamless ligation" procedures that leave no signatures of human manipulation.*"(45) This message was reinforced by veteran geneticist Dr. Michael Antoniou of King's College and Guy's

Hospital in London who even exclaimed: *"I have been doing this sort of things for many years in my studies of various regulation of gene expression... any molecular biologists will tell you that they can manipulate without leaving any scar behind".* [46]

Sure enough, techniques exist for manipulating a virus's nucleic acids that are known for being indistinguishable from what mother nature does, and for which I'll present just a few short examples:

Directed Evolution: Genetic engineers artificially recreate a large number of viral proteins, called spikes — now known to the public as those harpoons that stick out of viruses, which are used by it to latch onto cells. These new spikes are made to mutate randomly. They are then selected by the scientist on the basis of which ones have "learned," through continued mutation, to best attack the human receptors called ACE2, rendering them highly infective. Since the mutations in the spikes are completely random, no one would ever be able to suspect the work of a laboratory.

Phage Display Libraries: The same result is obtained by using a so-called bacteriophage, or a phage for short, which is a virus that infects bacteria. It can be engineered to produce Spike Proteins on its surface that have different hooks at the end (the Receptor Binding Domains). It's cultivated in human cell cultures in order to see which will attach themselves most effectively to the ACE2 receptors, infecting them. When the phages revealing the most virulent spikes are selected, the whole complex can be used to make a new virus. Once again, since the selection is spontaneous, even if forced in a lab, there is no trace of human intervention.

Seamless Ligation: It's a technique that allows one to insert pieces of DNA much more easily into another genome. For example, if researchers want to create so-called *recombinant* DNA, in which pieces of another DNA are introduced to create a completely new biological product, they have to carry out a process of cutting and pasting that often involves unwanted imprecisions. The Seamless Ligation technique, on the other hand, allows one to obtain a new DNA sequence in which the cut and pasted seams are not visible. When used to modify a virus, analysis of its genome will not show any trace of the human hand.

Viral infectivity adaptation studies: Finally, it's equally possible to manipulate viruses by simply allowing them to replicate and change in cell cultures that have human ACE2 receptors. Alternatively, they can be cultivated in so-called humanized—therefore, made to resemble our body—mice. With time the virus will know how to adapt on its own in order to effectively infect those cells, turning itself into a microbe that will be extremely virulent to humans and in which no trace of manipulation is visible.

In conclusion it should be easily understood that the scientific assessment which from the very beginning correctly pointed to SARS-CoV-2 being a laboratory escape has always been disingenuously contested by those arguing that any manipulation by so called *"Frankenstein science"* always leave scars behind as visible as those of Mary Shelley's monster. Also, the spotlight should not be exclusively pointed at Gain of Function or Gain of Function of concern, as the accidental infection of someone working in a laboratory, from the scientific directors to the humblest janitor, during even ordinary molecular studies that can possibly hide all traces of manipulation from any given Sherlock Holmes, has been and continues to be more than enough to place humans under grave threat.

Flipping Occam's Razor

The world-famous Occam's razor, from the 14th-century philosopher and theologist William of Occam, taught modern thought that, in simplified terms, there's no need to complicate an explanation when it can be simple and still perfectly serve its aim. Already in January 2020, at the explosion of the first SARS-CoV-2 infections in China, the media and politicians ran to open the files on its cousin epidemic, SARS-CoV-1 of 2003, and seeing that its origins were zoonotic (originating in bats and moving to humans), then, according to the above principle, an animal origin had to be the most obvious explanation for this new pestilence as well. Why complicate things, provoking Occam's ire? If only a few years earlier a cursed respiratory microbe fell from the faeces of a bat into the mouth of a civet cat and finally moved from that animal to us — well then it could be considered case closed, right?

Not at all.

What didn't quite make sense for many renowned researchers was that even the mainstream of science, particularly the so called talk show scientists, had in a blink of an eye accepted that rushed simplification. A reader who has absorbed what I have described thus far about certain laboratory practices, about the concerning rationale that inspires them, about the concrete dangers of killer pathogens escaping from those facilities, and finally, my references to the unsettling biological qualities of this new virus —subjects that make up the wide-ranging scientific examinations offered in this book— will clearly understand how hasty the media, politics, and science itself were in declaring zoonosis as the all-but certain cause of Covid-19 in all public opinion, a thesis still upheld today despite clear evidence to the contrary. Unfortunately, things are much more complicated when it comes to the investigation into the origin of SARS-CoV-2. Even before the world fell prey to the pandemic, there were already certain *liaisons dangereuses* in full swing between scientists and deadly viruses that reside in bats, especially coronaviruses. It's time to talk about those…

Batman, Batwoman, Bats, Institutions and Strange Clubs

For a few years now, it's been in vogue to refer to Northern California when thinking about the vanguard of the Politically Correct, of the movement for LGBTQ rights, or the most ideological fringes of the #Metoo movement, and Google Walkouts, which saw the tech giant of Silicon Valley taken to task by its employees on issues such as pay disparities between sexes, sexual harassment at work, or the obligation to resolve allegations regarding the latter through internal arbitration. In short, one thinks of the most driven part of the American liberal left, offspring of the Californian pacifism of the 60s. Geographically, the historical capital of this part of the planet is the city of Berkeley, where the university with the same name is located. If you are asking yourself what all of this has to do with Covid-19 and its origins, well, it's easy to explain.

It was the beginning of February 2020, in Europe almost nothing had happened but the media was mentioning a new epidemic in China that had worrying similarities to SARS from 2003, which had started from the spillover of a bat virus onto an intermediate species and finally onto humans. Around then I stumbled upon a very interesting article published by the scientific journal *eLife* which illustrated the prodigious immune system of bats against some of the deadliest viruses in history (Ebola, MERS, Marburg, SARS, Rabies), which as a result tend not to cause any illness in them. Unfortunately, these pathogens, however, finding themselves continually under attack by the merciless immune system of the nocturnal flying animals, react inside them by mutating frenetically in order to survive and, even while remaining innocuous to bats, they acquire deadly characteristics that can then massacre other species onto which those viruses sometimes jump. [47] The first contributors to this study were Dr. Cara Brook and her colleague Dr. Mike Boots of Berkeley University in California. I'll specify that this was important research, being part of the Bat One Health project which held within its scope Madagascar, Ghana, Bangladesh, and Australia, and which for years has attempted to understand if there is a link between the alterations in the habitat of bats and their dangerous tendency to spread lethal microbes in the environment. [48]

In any case, it was while perusing these lines that two names jumped out to me: DARPA and EcoHealth. The first is the most advanced military research laboratory of the US Department of Defense, the full name of which is the Defense Advanced Research Projects Agency, where the latest technologies are looked at inside out in order to obtain from them futuristic weapons. As a federal agency, for years it has had the power also to finance civil scientific research in every sector, just as long as there is something to be gained for the "National Security" of the country. Not infrequently the opposite has taken place, and DARPA military technologies have had major outcomes on civil society, as in the case of the first internet "backbone."

Either way, what interests us is that the study by Cara Brook as part of the Bat One Health project on the ferocious pathogenicity of bat viruses in other mammals was also to a large extent financed by DARPA. And it was here that things started not to add up. The first point: as stated above, in the area of Northern California between Silicon Valley and Berkeley University reigns the most advanced pacifistic progressivism in America, and so one has to wonder how, in the era of Google Walkouts where ethical questions have assumed absolute importance, that university could justify taking money from those who invent lethal weapons for a living. Second point: what does the "National Security" of the USA have to do with what flows in the veins of bats?

It was precisely the jarring collaboration between the military-industrial complex and the Californian "peaceniks" that pushed me to write to DARPA and to Dr. Brook for clarifications.

The scientist never replied to me despite repeated requests. American Defence replied immediately, in the person of Jared Adams, head of communications at DARPA. He told me right away two things: *"Our Biological Technologies Office (BTO) is helping the Department of Defense to counter novel forms of bioterrorism, deploy innovative biological countermeasures to protect U.S. forces, and accelerate warfighter readiness and overmatch to confront adversary threats. The study of zoonotic diseases is squarely in that mission space"*. Then: *"The teams will collect samples from animal reservoirs in the field for analysis in secure, bio-contained facilities; some teams will also conduct analysis on existing banked samples and datasets"*. (49)

It was therefore confirmed: they finance studies on viruses in bats, gathering samples exactly as they were doing in the Biosafety Level 4 lab in Wuhan, and they do this in various places throughout the world. Only the aim is different. But it's time to explain to the readers the first of the two end points of this brief digression on DARPA and Cara Brook. This book reveals, particularly from now on, the most dramatic backstories of Covid-19 which were never fully disclosed to the public, and the true nature of this coronavirus that causes it. The spotlight is inescapably pointed at Wuhan and on China as a country, where the pandemic exploded. But what has just been recounted should serve to remind us that if we want to nip in the bud the next devastating pandemic, the view of the investigators must scrutinize at 360 degrees, and yes, include the military both in China and in the rest of the world. Accidents in even the most ironclad labs, as I've already written, are unfortunately quite frequent.

There remains *EcoHealth* and Dr. Boots, which bring us directly back to the second end point of the DARPA-Cara Brook story and to the title of this subchapter.

It's *EcoHealth*, or rather *EcoHealth Alliance*, that lead us to

Batman, then to *Batwoman*, then to the serious critical nature of another institution of even more imposing dimensions than DARPA, the WHO, and finally to a number of embarrassing imbroglios in the upper echelons of science itself. But let's put together the mosaic: Dr. Mike Boots is the biologist from Berkeley University who signed along with the above mentioned Dr. Cara Brook the study on the extraordinary immune system of bats, which was part of the research of the *Bat One Health* project financed in part by DARPA, and thereby the Department of Defence. Boots, in February of 2020 — that is, in the first fatal days of the Covid-19 outbreak in the West— signed a petition with twenty-four American and Chinese colleagues calling for better collaboration between the two countries in the study of emergent viral infections. [(50)] Today it's evident that such an initiative can be situated within an entire series of prominent publications in the world's scientific community that appeared one after the other between January and February 2020 in a sudden showing of closeness between Western and Chinese researchers, among which was one that has now become notorious because it was clearly staged, that is orchestrated, as I'll point out further ahead. Ranks already began to close among the scientific journals that count, becoming a wall that has consistently kept out any inconvenient scientific research about the origins of this disaster, despite the authoritativeness of whoever presented them, as the academics and researchers who've written this book with me can attest.

Instead, the appeal of the professor from Berkeley and other colleagues was immediately published by the scientific journal *EcoHealth*, published by an NGO based in New York called *EcoHealth Alliance*, the patron of which is our *Batman*, aka Dr. Peter Daszak, an incredibly influential zoologist and ecologist who was a high-ranking member of the WHO team put in charge of investigating the origins of SARS-CoV-2 in China at the beginning of 2021. Daszak is *Batman* because he was the one to personally fight to obtain millions of dollars in finances from the United States government, and not only once but twice, to fund the work of the famous *Batwoman*: namely, Dr. Zheng-Li Shi, the super-specialist of coronaviruses in bats from the Biosafety Level 4 lab in Wuhan. Zheng-Li and her Wuhan Institute of Virology (WIV) are today in the eye of the storm for the origin of the Covid-19 pandemic, for reasons that have been brilliantly summarized by, among others, Virginie Courtier, an evolutionary biologist from the French CNRS and the Istitut Jaques-Monod at the University of Paris: "*...the deleted databases containing thousands of virus sequences—why the furin cleavage site was not described in the first Nature paper—how the sequence of the closely related virus RaTG13 was assembled—the full sequence of WIV15 and the full sequence of the eight coronaviruses collected by the Wuhan Institute of Virology in the same mine as RaTG13*". (51) Furthermore, as previously mentioned, what made the official stance of the WIV and of Dr Zheng-Li even more untenable was the intense Gain of Function research activity on coronaviruses they were known to be conducting.

But Daszak and his NGO succeeded anyway in financing Batwoman's questionable work, with a total of 7.4 million dollars from the US National Institutes of Health (NIH) on top of further funding from a US$ 200 million budget earmarked US State Department, even bypassing the moratorium on the American financing of this kind of research when labelled *of concern* enacted by President Obama in 2014 and only partially revoked by Trump in 2017. (52) In fact at the outbreak of the present pandemic the Administration of the last US President had realized the embarrassing intermingling of US taxpayers' moneys with Gain of Function in China and blocked the second tranche Peter Daszak was due to hand over to Zheng-Li Shi. However in the context of the red-hot contraposition that had

Donald Trump elevated as hate figure number one in America, such a move was chastised by the majority of the American media as a brutal attack against a noble scientific endeavour lead by *EcoHealth Alliance* in cooperation with Chinese researchers in the fight against the new pestilence. As a matter of fact the NIH then reinstated the funding in August 2020. In a written personal exchange with me Rutgers University molecular biologist Prof Richard Ebright made the following biting comment: "*Peter Daszak has been the frontman and bagman for the Wuhan Institute of Virology. He is an unusual character. He does not do research and does not have a lab. He is, essentially, a professional grant coordinator who coordinates multi-performance-site, multi-investigator mega-grants, in exchange for salary from the grants and in exchange for honorary authorships on research papers from the investigators receiving funds from the grants. Daszak has lied, brazenly and repeatedly, about facts relevant to the origins of Covid-19 and about facts relevant to his conflicts of interest.*"

Having said this, and way above the sphere of influence of Peter Daszak, both the National Institutes of Health (NIH) and the National Institute of Allergies and Infectious Diseases (NIAID), the latter historically headed by Dr. Anthony Fauci, managed to keep a US taxpayers credit line open for several viral Gain of Function experiments by exploiting a tiny clause written as Note.1 in the small print of the Obama moratorium, this: "*An exception from the research pause may be obtained if the head of the USG funding agency determines that the research is urgently necessary to protect the public health or national security.*" (53) The USG funding agencies are precisely the NIH and the NIAID.

In all this the aiding and abetting role of Dr Fauci is out in the open. As a matter of fact in 2017 Donald Trump had announced the so called *Potential Pandemic Pathogens Control and Oversight Framework* (P3CO) that mandated a regular risk-benefit review of each Gain-of-Function of concern experiments. The snag was that the P3CO Framework fully relied on those wishing to fund such experiments to asses their risk-benefit ratio, in a glaring conflict of interest situation. In fact Anthony Fauci and his colleague at the NIH Francis Collis never once implemented the P3CO requirement. Again, a comment by Prof Richard Ebright: "*Twice, we succeeded in breaking through and securing national-level policy changes: in 2014 with the Pause, and in 2017 with the P3CO Framework. But at every step along the way, we were opposed, tooth and nail, by the NIAID Director, Anthony Fauci and by the small coterie of scientists, just one to two dozen, with vested interests in high-risk research on pathogens. And each time we succeeded in breaking through and bringing about policy changes, the NIAID Director first subverted, and then nullified, the policy change as soon as policy-makers turned their attention elsewhere.*"

Then Ebright strikes a highly controversial note: "*The $70 million dollars in USAID, DARPA, DTRA, and DHS contracts and subcontacts awarded to EcoHealth Alliance over the past ten years appear likely to have been part of an intelligence-gathering scheme in which US intelligence and defence agencies provided funds, with EcoHealth Alliance as cut-out, to overseas labs performing bioweapons-agents research, in the hope this might enable US intelligence and defence agencies to monitor progress in overseas labs performing bioweapons-agents research. If so, the scheme was a catastrophic failure with unprecedented blowback, yielding no actionable intelligence, and possibly triggering a pandemic that killed more than 600,000 in the US, devastated the US economy, and grievously damaged the US geopolitical position.*"

The Rutgers University Professor stops a millimetre short of mentioning Anthony Fauci again, but the inference is clear.

So, let's recap what is manifest so far: for six years, and even after the outbreak of the worst pandemic in a century, the top health agencies in the US – that is Francis Collins' NIH and Anthony Fauci's NIAID – did finance Gain of Function precisely at the Wuhan Institute of Virology led by *Batwoman* Dr Zheng-Li Shi, in violation of two US presidential orders to block or limit such funding; the "*bagman*" that delivered the moneys to Wuhan is *Batman* Peter Daszak, president of the New York based *EcoHealth Alliance* and a central figure in the narrative that staunchly pedalled the natural origin theory for SARS-CoV-2 despite the absence of true scientific evidence: the funds that Daszak funnelled to the WIV were no doubt destined to Gain of Function studies as proven by the NIH documents this book cites in note 52.

Lastly, a renowned researcher like Prof Richard Ebright accused Fauci to have doggedly and repeatedly thrown spanners in the wheels of the scientific community's attempts to limit viral Gain of Function of concern both internationally and in China.

In the light of the above, the revelations about a confidential meeting that took place on February 1, 2020, comprising Dr Anthony Fauci and several champions of Covid-19's zoonosis come as no surprise. On that occasion a pretty odd scientific U-turn took place in a matter of just a few hours: initially records show that most participants were openly discussing how SARS-CoV-2's features did point to a non natural origin, but then just few hours later the same panel of experts released a public statement where they solemnly upheld the very opposite conclusion.

The basic facts of this extraordinary turnabout were published by *BuzzFeed News* at the beginning of June 2021 after it obtained a large number of private emails involving Anthony Fauci thanks to a Freedom of Information request, later published all over the international media. Here are the main facts for those that may have missed this crucial episode: at the end of January 2020, a few hours past the WHO official declaration that a new coronavirus pandemic was under way, the NIAID director is exchanging via emails at first, then in a web conference, with a group of peers among which the most prominent is the California Scripps Research Institute's Kristian Andersen, but the influential Jeremy Farrar, who leads the Wellcome Trust of London and is the man in charge of substantial funding for both researchers and scientific publications, is also present. What they initially are saying to each other is that the genetic makeup of SARS-CoV-2 is not at all consistent with natural evolution, thus the laboratory origin seems the favourite hypothesis. However just three days later Kristian Andersen will word an official statement reaffirming the zoonotic origin of the virus, which from that moment onwards will become the official Gospel for the natural origin of the Covid-19 pandemic. What happened is such a short timespan cannot have anything to do with any scientific validation of such a hellishly complex biological conundrum, a process that normally takes months or even years. Anthony Fauci would never have made public his own very early doubts on the zoonotic theory if he had not been caught with his hands in the proverbial cookie jar by *BuzzFeed News* reporters. However the almost 8 million US$ he repeatedly funnelled into the coffers of the Wuhan Institute of Virology to fund high risk coronavirus manipulations in the years before the pandemic outbreak speak volumes about the turnabout that followed the confidential February the 1st exchanges. A veteran and world renowned virologist who asked to remain anonymous, but whose statements are in my possession, thus described Anthony Fauci: *"He is a narcissistic megalomaniac and far too powerful. I had a long chat with a senior US researcher recently, who hates having to be nice to him and toe the line, however he has to or his institute won't get funded. Fauci runs a dictatorship and can sign off large multi-million dollar grants without going through the peer review grant system. He has to go."*

The fact remains that the flow of cash between Peter Daszak and Dr. Zheng-Li Shi kept going unhindered from 2014 till April 2020. Then this scientist had an even worse effect as an outspoken defender and financial mentor of Zheng-Li Shi. But first, a final point: who is Dr. Christian Drosten? Well, he's another central author in Cara Brook's study, but we can also find him in the role of senior editor employed by Daszak at *EcoHealth*, as well as entangled again in a glaring case of pro-Chinese editorial deceit published in *The Lancet*, no less, and once again at the order of Dr. Daszak. We'll talk about it shortly but as you can see the revolving doors are fully in place in this story.

The moment has come to focus on the crucial role that *EcoHealth Alliance* played in obfuscating every international attempt at arriving at the true origins of Covid-19, assisted in this case by an unprecedented public relations campaign waged by the Chinese government in the all important social media and scientific journals in order to sideline what already then was growing evidence against the natural origin theory for Covid-19.

What Got into Them?

A brief, necessary preamble: most of the general public—through no fault of their own—lacks an awareness of how science, research, medicine, pharmacology and, consequentially, public health, plus the training of doctors and treatments are carried out and obtained. The actors at the top of the pyramid are actually not universities, hospitals, pharmaceutical or diagnostic/medical industries, nor are they the State-run regulatory institutions. There is an almost obligatory step for each of these to then proceed, which is the publication of one's findings in so-called *peer-reviewed* scientific journals. In other words, a significant majority of what science produces is taken seriously only if it passes through the filter of these publications and the revision of one's results by other scientists *(peer-review)*.

Here we're not interested in the merits or demerits of this system. What matters to us is for readers to realize the importance this is granted in order to then understand some central factors in the investigation into the scandals and true crimes surrounding Covid-19. Obviously those magazines have publishers, who are just as powerful as the ones behind the mass media and social networks who, on the contrary, are well known to the public — after all, we're talking about nothing short of the health of billions of humans and of multibillion-dollar industries as a result. For this reason, we citizens, in theory, should be able to recognize on the fly names of publishers such as *Springer Nature* and *Elsevier,* and then journals like *Nature, PLoS One, Science, The Lancet, BioEssays, Cell* or acronyms such as *BMJ, NEJM, PNAS,* but there are many of them and I won't overdo it. What matters is that the concepts cited above are clear, because in this viral tragedy the games that count are all played in the pages of *peer-reviewed* scientific journals. The following illustrates as much.

Truly, this virus does things never seen before, and not only on a biological level. In fact, institutions that have written the history of science and governed excellently over the health of millions of people have allowed themselves to lose their credibility, at least in part, when faced with the question: *Where did Covid-19 come from?* And not just a few people, observing some of their embarrassing behaviours, have wondered *What got into them?*

There's only one possible answer: fear of China. It's not hard to see this. There would be unheard-of financial and legal repercussions for Beijing if, first of all, global public opinion was allowed to understand why the natural origin of the pandemic never was a viable theory to begin with, and if the lies and omissions by China which form a part of this volume well beyond the discussion on the accidental lab-leak of SARS-CoV-2 were to be internationally recognised. But then, who has an interest in pinning the world's second superpower back against a wall in the name of the full truth and not just chunks or scraps of it? Essentially no one. China on its own produces 12.4% of everything that's traded in the world [54], with the US and Germany behind in line. And not only gadgets, cell phones, clothing, and various plastic items, as most people imagine: to give an example, for years the American FDA has been sending warnings to the White House over the United States' heavy dependency on medical drugs and equipment produced in China, [55] and let's not forget that this Asian superpower is also growing to become a colossal customer for our goods and services. Finally, taking the country head on to force out of her admissions for crimes that are way more damning than the accidental laboratory leak of SARS-CoV-2 would worsen even further the already crippled worldwide economy, which is a taboo for politicians and for business alike. This is, therefore, *"what got into them"*.

Then, as the incipit of this book clearly states, there's little doubt today that the majority of the news media, including the scientific journals and the top echelon of most supranational organizations like the WHO, had joined forces during the 2020 US election year to dethrone Donald Trump, the "Chinese virus" President, the standard bearer of US unilateralism. Therefore it was anathema for virtually anyone to be pointing the finger at Chinese science as the reckless source of the pandemic because that, in the heated political climate of the day, equated in most respectable circles to oiling Trump's march into a second term in office. Thus what follows.

Let's get to the facts, starting with three of the most prestigious and authoritative scientific journals of all time, The *Lancet, PLOS Pathogens,* and *Nature*. I'll begin with the last two. In the span of a week in May 2020, they published the well-known "Pangolin Papers" [56], scientific studies that aimed to confirm in the eyes of the world — the eyes that "counted"—that the intermediary species from which SARS-CoV-2 jumped to humans were the pangolins. But they short-lived. They were obviously incomplete studies, not even allowing for independent verification, a fact that is very serious in the sciences. The embarrassment reached its apex when the directors of *PLOS Pathogens, Nature,* and one of the editors of the first study, a virologist from Iowa University, Prof Stanley Perlman, had to admit to the debacle. I wrote to the latter, and he confirmed as much: *"Paolo, What I can say is that there are issues with the papers and that they are under investigation by the journals. The issues may be serious but the extent of the problem is not fully determined yet."* (57) What had propelled such prestigious names to hurriedly produce this kind of mess with fallacious studies in order to provide support for the natural-origin theory of the virus? But a considerable amount of time before, it was *The Lancet* that hit rock bottom, and who was mixed up in it? As always, it was *Batman*.

The truth came to light when in November 2020 the American NGO *U.S. Right to Know* published the following: *"Emails obtained by U.S. Right to Know show that a statement in The Lancet authored by 27 prominent public health scientists condemning "conspiracy theories suggesting that Covid-19 does not have a natural origin" was organized by employees of EcoHealth Alliance, a non-profit group that has received millions of dollars received of U.S. taxpayer funding to genetically manipulate coronaviruses with scientists at the Wuhan Institute of Virology."* (58) *EcoHealth Alliance* again, therefore *Peter Daszak*.

The publication date of this falsehood in *The Lancet* demonstrates what I have just written above, namely that *"Ranks already began to close among the scientific journals that count"*: it was February 19, 2020, just a few days earlier the WHO had given a name to the pandemic and already Daszak and associates were working to obfuscate the debate concerning its origins.

The title was overt: *Statement in support of the scientists, public health professionals, and medical professionals of China combatting Covid-19.* (59) The brazenness of their declarations were even more extreme: *"... the scientists, public health professionals, and medical professionals of China, in particular, have worked diligently and effectively to rapidly identify the pathogen behind this outbreak... and share their results transparently with the global health community*" (ibidem), statements that would be drastically contradicted precisely by the WHO's farcical inquiry in China into the origins of the virus a year later conducted under the suffocating supervision of the Chinese Communist Party, which dictated a priori every move while the above mentioned Chinese scientists kept silent and mountains of crucial scientific data disappeared. But the editorial spoke firmly: "*We stand together to strongly condemn conspiracy theories suggesting that Covid-19 does not have a natural origin. Scientists from multiple countries have published and analysed genomes of the causative agent, severe acute respiratory syndrome coronavirus 2 (SARS-CoV-2), and they overwhelmingly conclude that this coronavirus originated in wildlife*" (ibidem), thereby another affirmation lacking in any scientific foundation, to the point that to this day it is still supported by incomplete science. The emails obtained by U.S. *Right to Know* reveal our *Batman's* fraudulent intentions, when they write that he wanted the editorial to "*not be identifiable as coming from any one organization or person*" but rather to be seen as "*simply a letter from leading scientists.*" [60] A final torpedo to the prestige of *The Lancet* are the signatures: 27 scientists, all aware of the fact that among them, the professors John Mackenzie, Hume Field, Christian Drosten, James Hughes, Rita Colwell, and William Karesh were and are part of the salaried staff of *EcoHealth Alliance* and of its scientific journal *EcoHealth*, all under the reign of Peter Daszak, who created an intense lobby to finance precisely the number one suspected laboratory in the world for the escape of the virus, the Wuhan Institute of Virology (WIV), and for that reason had a strong interest in running aground all doubts about the natural origin of SARS-CoV-2. The false editorial concluded with the brazen line: "*We declare no competing interests.*" (ibidem)

But to explain the complacent silence of the scientific publishers that count — at the end of the day, we're essentially talking about the big ones, Springer-Nature and Elsevier — regarding the inquiries into the origin of Covid-19, there is another factor in addition to geopolitical trepidations and the work of certain characters: the money that Beijing is pouring into the pockets of the above mentioned publishing houses. China is the main sponsor of the so-called Open Access scientific publications, both at Springer-Nature and Elsevier, ahead of every other country by a large margin, for a total of 77 journals sponsored and financed at a rate of over 20 million dollars per year, on top of which are other less accountable Chinese contributions to what are known as "hybrid and paid journals." *The Lancet* and *Nature* belong to the former of these two categories. [(61)]

After the questionable activity of the large scientific publishing groups, the story continues with the World Health Organization (WHO), which also lent itself to shamefully accommodating China, precisely in regards to the inquiry into the true origins of SARS-CoV-2. And again a large crowd of international experts had to ask, *What got into them?*

They Tried

In terms of the embarrassing way the WHO bent down before Beijing, which culminated in its farcical "mission" in China on the origins of Covid-19 between January and February 2021, my *warm-up* for readers is rather concise —just a few crucial points, since the story has been extensively reported by some media outlets. However this book cannot ignore it.

Now, it would be all too easy for me to discredit the WHO mission by telling you that China had been given the power to approve the members from the international scientific community who took part in it, and the only American who was allowed to participate was our very own *Batman*... Peter Daszak, [(62)] the "turbo-charged" sponsor of none other than the

Chinese research institute that the team should have investigated more than any other place in the world, the Wuhan Institute of Virology (WIV), in a conflict of interests visible from the moon. Unfortunately, however, things went much worse. For the sake of brevity I'll simply list the fundamental scientific information to which the international members of the WHO mission did not have access, due to the incontestable refusal of the Chinese authorities, and to which they gave in:

- The clinical files and the biological samples of 174 cases of some of the earliest suspected SARS-CoV-2 infections at the beginning of December 2019 in the city of Wuhan, which were fundamental for uncovering where such infections had come from (China? abroad?) or if any of these patients had worked, in any capacity, at the WIV. (63)
- The possibility of verifying clinical files of generic hospitalizations in Hubei province up to several months before December 2019, in order to see if anything had been ignored or erroneously interpreted by the medical staff and which could, looking back, resemble Covid-19. The Chinese presented only their own final conclusions: nothing of suspicious nature, take it or leave it. (ibidem)
- To the so-called raw data on which the Chinese scientists had based the studies requested by the international community, which they presented to the WHO mission. In the sciences, it is impossible to verify the legitimacy of a study if one is kept in the dark about its primary sources. (ibidem)
- Access not only to the medical records, but actually to blood banks and samples taken from the respiratory tract of patients treated before December 2019 for disparate pathologies not clearly attributable to Covid-19. (ibidem)
- The examination of samples of sewage fluids taken in central China before December 2019. Local authorities said

that they had destroyed them, which would be something considerably rare in any modern public hygiene system. They were fundamental for tracing any hypothetical fragments of the SARS-CoV-2 virus which, as is well known, is found in human waste. (ibidem)

- The analysis of databases of various Chinese research institutes that contained thousands of viral sequences, in order to verify the similarities of the genomes with SARS-CoV-2 nucleic acids and perhaps even confirm the natural origin of the pandemic… or the exact opposite. It's estimated that for the WHO mission a total of 16,000 samples taken from bats and yet-unpublished coronavirus genetic sequences were labeled inaccessible. [64]
- The independent analysis of the exact genetic sequence of the so-called parent virus to SARS-CoV-2, RATG13, and of the sequences of an additional eight coronaviruses uncovered by the WIV in the same mine from which precisely RATG13 apparently originally came. (ibidem)
- Confidential interviews with the personnel of Chinese laboratories that study and manipulate coronaviruses, including technicians, maintenance workers, custodians, those in charge of waste and hygiene, security, plus those caring for the laboratory animals, office workers, and obviously researches and students. [65]

To sum up, I believe that the cage in which the WHO accepted operating —and it's already well known that the international experts had no freedom of movement and/or action, as they were continuously supervised by local agents — speaks for itself; but it's too fitting to not share the biting observation of Prof David Relman of Stanford University, published in *The Washington Post* at the end of the useless field trip the WHO team took in search of the pandemic's origins: *"If the only information you're allowing to be weighed is provided by the very people who have everything to lose by revealing such evidence, that just doesn't come close to passing the sniff test".* (66)

Proof that the WHO mission had been stifled from the get go can be found in black and white in the document *WHO-convened Global Study of the Origins of SARS-CoV-2. Terms of References for the China Part* (67), namely the terms of conduct, the limits of the investigation, and the suffocating geographical confines that China imposed on the international community before allowing any investigation whatsoever in its territory. It is not even that long to read, but it truly does confirm, with each written letter, the words of Relman quoted above. And so, what is there left to say about this embarrassing chapter of an institution, the World Health Organization, which humiliated itself before the power of Beijing's GDP at the cost of global public interest? Maybe only this: "*The report shows why having the Beijing government co-investigate a possible lab leak and deadly cover up is like asking the Kremlin to co-investigate Chernobyl.*" This was written by Dr. Jamie Metzl, an actual member of the WHO's advisory committee on human genome editing, and one of the scientists who organized the open letter *"Call For A Full Investigation Into The Origins of Covid-19"* which appeared in *The New York Times* on April 7, 2021. (68)

The WHO, one could say, tried to pass off a farce for an investigation. We still have to ask ourselves who among its ranks could have imagined that the world would have fallen for it.

The Most "Unnatural" Nature Ever Seen in a Human Virus

In this final part of my introduction to the book, I'd like to warm-up your mental muscles in order to confront the heart of this volume as illustrated by Angus Dalgleish and Steven Quay. Namely the pieces of scientific proof – called in technical terms, "*molecular evidence*" – to support both the dramatic accusations we bring against the Chinese authorities and to demonstrate the presence at the heart of SARS-CoV-2 of the engineered lethal molecular machinery that brought devastation around the world.

Unfortunately, here, as they say, there's no getting around it, meaning that the material has to be illustrated with a solid dose of cellular, molecular, and genetic biology, with the risk of otherwise being accused by experts of inaccurate or even falsified points. For my part, I'll be as linear as possible, with examples and metaphors to help simplify things; the two scientific co-authors of this book will certainly have softened to a great extent their prose, but it's worthwhile following this scientific information because what it reveals about the nature of the virus that has paralyzed the world is, truly, shocking and from that point on everything one can read about this catastrophe becomes something else entirely. This brings us back to Wuhan, in the first days of that cursed year.

Why on January 3, 2020, precisely during the first early signs of the pandemic, did the Chinese government order the Wuhan Institute of Virology to destroy the samples of SARS-CoV-2 that they had isolated? Only two days earlier another order from Beijing had been given to the director of the Institute, Dr. Yanyi Wang, namely to take down from Social media the information on Covid-19 and to keep quiet about it with the press. (69) News concerning the disappearance and/or arrest of citizens and human rights lawyers in China who were active in directly sharing on social media what was happening in Wuhan accumulated in those weeks in the pages of the *Financial Times, Business Insider, The Guardian*, not to mention in a whole slew of accounts on Twitter, Weibo et al. (70) These facts, already noteworthy in and of themselves, acquire particular relevance if one considers that just a few weeks later the same central government in Beijing would distance itself from the hypothesis that the virus had infected humans in the now famous Huanan market in Wuhan: the tests carried out there didn't uncover any connection between the animals for sale and the virus, as was revealed in a note by Dr. Gao Fu, director of the Chinese Center for Disease Control and Prevention. [71]

So already at the beginning of the pandemic China was showing the world two things: on one hand, it was impossible for it to continue to maintain the convenient theory of the unfortunate and innocent double leap of SARS-CoV-2 from a bat to another animal to humans in a city market; on the other, the central authorities had rushed some time earlier to gag the exact laboratory that, in the same geographical area, conserved and edited bat coronaviruses, along with whomever tried to tell inconvenient truths to the international community. But what Beijing could no longer hide, because it had already spread across the world, was the molecular structure of SARS-CoV-2 that was responsible for the Covid-19 pandemic, and already in the first few weeks of its spread a few authoritative scientists had noticed in it some suspiciously and even disturbingly strange qualities.

For example, an American team from the Broad Institute at MIT and Harvard and from the University of British Columbia in Canada published the following in May 2020: *"In a side-by-side comparison of evolutionary dynamics between the 2019/2020 SARS-CoV-2 and the 2003 SARS-CoV, we were surprised to find that SARS-CoV-2 resembles SARS-CoV in the late phase of the 2003 epidemic after SARS-CoV had developed several advantageous adaptations for human transmission. Our observations suggest that by the time SARS-CoV-2 was first detected in late 2019, it was already pre-adapted to human transmission to an extent similar to late epidemic SARS-CoV. However, no precursors or branches of evolution stemming from a less human-adapted SARS-CoV-2-like virus have been detected."* [72]

To translate: one must understand that any virus that jumps from any species to another has to do some work to adapt to the new host before it can infect it effectively. The virologists therefore expect to find, at some point during its evolution, some clumsier cousins that were discarded over time, until the eventual appearance of the version that succeeded in developing sufficient characteristics to adapt well to the new host. When SARS became an epidemic danger, its cousins, which came earlier, were uncovered and described in detail, allowing one to see how they gradually evolved in order to adapt to living in humans with ever-growing efficacy, an adaptive process that reached its apex at the end of the epidemic in 2003. In the case of Covid-19, on the other hand, these cousins were never found; regardless, the virus seemed adapted to strike humans from the very start, as if it were the latest version of SARS: that is, magically appearing out of nowhere and ready to infect us without any gradual evolutionary history. Which would be truly strange, unless...

To explain the following, I'd like to remind readers of the so-called humanized mice in the context of techniques for viral genome editing that don't leave any trace of the scientists' intervention. This regards guinea pigs (mice) into which human genetic material is inserted in order to grow inside of them cells and tissues that are completely similar to ours, on which scientists can then conduct experiments that would be ethically impossible on people. In the case of Gain of Function with coronaviruses, the trick is to make the primary human receptor, called ACE2, grow on the outside of the mice's cells, allowing the virus to attack and invade them. The ACE2 receptor works like a lock on the outside of the cell, which allows a particular key in the possession of coronaviruses — the Spike Protein — to open an aperture through which they will infect that very cell. Therefore, going back to the humanized mice, they are given our cellular lock, the ACE2, and they are infected with the virus which is then left to replicate itself as long as is necessary for it to adapt to humanized cells, even in some cases for the time it takes for it to learn how to infect them with pandemic-level ferocity. And this brings as back to my "unless..." from the previous paragraph: if a coronavirus in bats, which is innocuous to humans, undergoes intensive "training" to infect humanized cells, and if then by an unfortunate accident it infects a researcher or slips out and into the environment as we know often happens, then yes, we would have on our hands a virus that came out of nowhere, an orphan with no natural evolutionary history that would immediately be effectively adapted for attacking the human population. Who, if not precisely the Wuhan Institute of Virology, was carrying out until December 2020 this exact kind of study? (73) And, on top of that, with the limited security measures that we have already discussed.

However, it's the same Chinese-WHO narrative about the zoonotic or natural origin of Covid-19 that in the case of the rapid adaptation of SARS-CoV-2 to humans shoots itself in the proverbial foot, when one considers the nature of this adaptation. In order to hold water, it needs to demonstrate that SARS-CoV-2, beginning as a virus in bats and then jumping to an intermediary animal and finally to humans, is, first of all, extremely well adapted to the first and the second animal... and it would be incredible if this wasn't the case. But it is not the case, as a whole series of molecular tests will show. In a study by Dr. Yuri Deigin and Dr. Rosanna Segreto published in *Environmental Chemistry Letters* on March 25, 2021, these two well-known researchers speak openly about the strange ability of the SARS-CoV-2 proteins to attach themselves with more ease onto human cells than onto those of other animals, a fact that in any textbook would suggest a spillover in the opposite direction, that is, from a human to an animal. (74) The last thrust comes when the researches confirm that even in the case of bats, the SARS-CoV-2 virus reveals itself to be less effective in infecting its ACE2 receptors than those of humans – another leak in the ship of the "official truth." In short, it doesn't check out that a pathogen with characteristics described up to this point – that is, considerably better adapted to humans than to bats or pangolins – could have jumped in nature from animals and then to people. The narrative supplied by China and the WHO falls apart on its own here, unless the entire ABC of biological science has to be rewritten.

Therefore, what we are seeing is that SARS-CoV-2 is bound by precise chemical and molecular steps in its fight to survive by infecting cells. And it's at this point that we find the second undeniable piece of evidence against the idea that SARS-CoV-2 evolved in nature and subsequently attacked us. Please, welcome *Mr. Furin Cleavage Site.*

Don't worry, it sounds more complicated than it is. Everything becomes simple if we remember what was stated just above and which I'll copy again almost identically, namely that *"the ACE2 receptor works as a lock on the outside of the cell that allows a particular key in the possession of coronaviruses – the Spike Protein – to open a hole through which they will infect that very cell."* Right, the keys are small metal rods which in order to work need to be cut. The sequence of cuts into the rod is a unique code that will be recognized exclusively by one lock. In the same way, the SARS-CoV-2 "Spike Protein-key" will have to be cut – *Cleavage* is just that – before it can open the lock in human cells called the ACE2 receptor. The incision made on the metal key is carried out by a machine at the key shop; the one on the SARS-CoV-2 "Spike Protein-key" by an enzyme called Furin. Therefore, the *Furin Cleavage Site* is the exact point (the *Site*) in the SARS-CoV-2 "Spike Protein-key" where the enzyme *Furin* cuts it so that it will work inside the lock to human cells, ACE2.

Now, to this process we only need to add a disturbing detail to fully grasp the nefarious nature of the pandemic: SARS-CoV-2 is the only coronavirus of its kind, which is to say, the only known Betacoronavirus, to have been endowed with this particularly tailored Cleavage, which has been placed in a very strategic point (the *Site*) of the Spike Protein called S1/S2 junction. I call everyone's attention to this fact, as it is precisely this *Site* that endows SARS-CoV-2 with its extraordinary and lethal powers to penetrate our cells. (75) As if someone, who isn't nature, had made it that way on purpose. Mind that this is not just a line for dramatic effect: on May 20, 2020 Dr. Alina Chan, genetic engineer from the Broad Institute of MIT and Harvard, informed the public on Twitter that a Gain of Function experiment in 2006 had inserted exactly a *Furin Cleavage Site* in the Spike Protein of an old SARS coronavirus. Therefore, a precedent for intentional manipulation by man using a Furin Cleavage Site existed, and this tells us a great deal. (76) But what's more, a study conducted at the University of Göttingen in Germany demonstrated at the end of the same month that if one deprives the Spike Protein, or the key, in SARS-CoV-2 of the incision of the enzyme in question, it will be largely disabled in its primary goal: to infect the cells in our lungs. (77) In other words, without that *Furin Cleavage Site* the deadly pandemic virus suddenly loses a good deal of its fire power. One should note that, in theory, what the German microbiologists' experiment did was, clearly, invert what is the point of arrival in a Gain of Function experiment, as you already know by now. And this also tells us a great deal.

To sum up: the coronavirus called SARS-CoV-2 appears out of nowhere, and infects human cells more easily than the cells of any other animal using a key called "Spike Protein-key" with the help of the *Furin Cleavage Site* which, oddly enough, only it possesses in the viral family to which it belongs, and which is a notorious trademark of laboratory manipulations aimed at greatly enhancing a virus infectivity. Lastly, without a *Furin Cleavage Site* SARS-CoV-2 loses virulence in relation to humans.

But in order to complete the picture of clues that give fuel to the suspicion that Gain of Function research could have been the origin of the pandemic, we're missing the answer to a decisive question, which is the following: ultimately does the *Furin Cleavage Site*, in addition to being what greatly helps this coronavirus to attack our lungs, also give it other *functional gains* to make it more pathogenic? The answer is a resounding yes. A study from the University of Minnesota (USA) confirmed as much in May 2020 in the pages of the prestigious publication *Proceedings of the National Academy of Sciences* (PNAS): the entry of SARS-CoV-2 into cells, the authors inform us, is pre-activated by the *Furin* enzyme, which along with two other factors *"allows SARS-CoV-2 to maintain efficient cell entry while evading immune surveillance."* And this last element is a dramatic functional gain compared to other coronaviruses. (78) But not just that: more functional gains are to be found in the pandemic virus that dreadfully amplify its pathogenicity and those will be explained later by the two scientific co-authors. As if that weren't enough, the above mentioned Yuri Deigin and Rosanna Segreto upped the ante when confirming that *"at the same time, Furin Cleavage Sites have been routinely inserted into coronaviruses in Gain-of-Function experiments."* (79)

It is vital at this point to reiterate with emphasis that an early disclosure of the presence in the novel coronavirus of the *Furin Cleavage Site* (and of further molecular details Angus Dalgleish is about to illustrate) when its action was limited to an epidemic in China would have no doubt allowed at least a section of the international medical and political world to grasp at once the magnitude of the threat and to enact containment policies that would have possibly saved countless lives. But this did not happen because, as previously hinted at, Dr Zheng-Li Shi, the chief virologist at the WIV who was the first to discover the Furin Cleavage Site, had to keep silent about it for months despite being fully aware of the foreboding associated with such biological weaponry in a virus. It was Dr Zheng-Li Shi who on the 3rd of

February 2020 had published in *Nature* the exclusive sequence of what she then called the 2019-nCoV, renamed afterwards SARS-CoV-2. She wrote : *"Here we report the identification and characterization of a new coronavirus (2019-nCoV), which caused an epidemic of acute respiratory syndrome in humans in Wuhan, China. The epidemic, which started on 12 December 2019, had caused 2,794 laboratory-confirmed infections including 80 deaths by 26 January 2020."* (80)

Firstly the date of that study tells us that it was researched between December 2019 and January 2020 (if not before), and this confirms that both the Chines virologist and her superiors in the Wuhan bureaucracy knew of the Furin Cleavage Site way before a pandemic engulfed the planet. Could they have missed it after such an in-depth sequencing? Well, a neurosurgeon said to me *"It'd be like I miss a bullet in the brain of a patient as I examine his CAT scan"*. It was Dr Virginie Courtier, an evolutionary biologist from the French CNRS and the Istitut Jaques-Monod at the University of Paris, who not long ago asked: *"...why the Furin Cleavage site was not described in the first Nature paper?"*, which takes for granted that Dr Zheng-Li knew exactly what she had seen in SARS-CoV-2 thanks to the cutting edge technology that the French themselves had helped the WIV to acquire. (81)

When I personally asked the already mentioned geneticist Michael Antoniou at King's College London if there was any chance of the Chinese virologist having missed the Furin Cleavage back in January 2020, he peremptorily replied *"Impossible"*.

Of the exact same opinion is Prof Bruno Canard, renowned microbiologist formerly with Harvard Medical School and today with Marseille University but also one of the authors of the first peer-reviewed study that identified the Furin Cleavage Site in CoV-2. In a very recent exchange with me, of which I have copy, he doubled down thus: *"This is mind bending... Do you really believe 29 other top virologists also missed it? Impossible to miss..."*

Secondly, as the study clearly states, the size of the contagion was at that point relatively insignificant compared with what lay ahead for humanity, so there was ample time to warn the scientific community and policymakers. Beijing did nothing. This kind of behaviour is beyond the pale for a partner of the interconnected world, worse, it's criminal on a historical scale and the partisan convulsions in America in the quest to defeat a politician all but strengthened this conspiracy of silence. Frankly, no further comment is needed at this point.... Or perhaps one ought to remind readers of the tragic fate of Li Wenliang, the Chinese ophthalmologist who first raised the alarm for an unknown respiratory disease he was observing in some Wuhan patients in the second half of 2019. He was brutally summoned to a police station where he was threatened, insulted and forced to sign an abjuratory statement on what he had very clearly spotted, COVID-19, the disease that ended up killing him shortly afterwards. This episode was not lost on Zheng-li Shi and her colleagues and speaks volumes about their obstinate silence.

The next section of proof brings us into an ultra-microscopic world, to a near-atomic level, in order to talk about the amino acids of the SARS-CoV-2 Spike Proteins. It is a rather painful section because every tear shed by humanity throughout the cursed months of the pandemic, every death, every agonizing hospitalization, every horrible convalescence including from Long Covid, and every exhausting lockdown, we owe precisely to the extraordinary ability of this coronavirus to open the locks of our cells in order to ravage them. But, for their part, the "Spike Protein-keys" owe their power to the precise – but I'll add, completely unnatural – arrangement of the amino acids around them. Let's quickly take another look at the molecular ABCs in order to understand this better.

Amino acids are truly the first bricks in biological life, because they are primarily composed of four foundational elements for the whole universe: hydrogen, oxygen, carbon and nitrogen. They are small molecules, which explains why in our investigation into the origins of Covid-19 we use the term "molecular evidence" when referring precisely to information about amino acids. The terrible "Spike Protein-key" in SARS-CoV-2 is, as already stated several times, just a protein and proteins are not anything but chains of amino acids. Therefore, the SARS-CoV-2 Spike Protein is a simple combination of amino acids, but what mostly interests us is the final part of the spike, which latches onto the ACE2 receptors of our cells. It ends with the two sections, the *Receptor Binding Domain* and the *Receptor Binding Motif,* where the term receptor binding always means *"the one that binds to the receptor"*. Keep this in mind for later.

Now just one essential notion needs to be acquired here, which few people know: the particular positive electric charge that SARS-CoV-2 Spike Proteins have. What's strange is not that it's there at all, but its intensity, which, once again, is unique to SARS-CoV-2 when compared to every other SARS virus.

This is the discovery that suddenly appeared to a group of researchers, including one of the contributors to this book, Prof Angus Dalgleish, while they were focusing on a completely different aim, namely creating a Covid vaccine. The team, at that point, had a classic moment of *putting two and two together:* already nature seemed to have miraculously endowed SARS-CoV-2 with the pathogenic *Furin Cleavage Site*, which is not normal for that kind of microbe; now, also the great anomaly that its *"Spike Protein-key"* is very much positively charged, which, as I'll soon explain, makes it even more dangerous. Too many incredibly rare qualities and all in one place, which is all truly unnatural, and – what a coincidence – all of them focused at infecting human cells more than the cells of any other studied animal, bats included. The following consideration was instinctively made by those scientists: are these not perhaps the qualities that Gain of Function experiments carried out at the Wuhan Institute of Virology sought to add to various coronaviruses which would be otherwise innocuous to humans? It seems that Dalgleish and his colleagues Birger Sorensen and Anders Susrud ran right into the idea that the virus was the product of a lab, while they weren't even looking for it. (82) I'll go back to the anomalous positive charge in simple terms, because it's fundamental for our inquiry.

We've all studied how there are electric charges in atoms (positive, negative, and neutral) which are essential for their existence. However, it does not come at all naturally for us to think that the signs + or – play fundamental roles even in the type of harm carried out by a viral infection. And yet that is, tragically, the way it is when dealing with Covid-19. As already stated, the SARS-CoV-2 Spike Protein reveals positive electric charges far superior to those of the SARS coronavirus from 2003, and these are what form "bridges" that attach to the membrane of the attacked cell, allowing Covid-19 to do more harm than predicted. (ibidem) In particular, what grants the spike of this pandemic virus this electric superpower seems to be unusually inserted groups of amino acids… but inserted by whom? And then there's the question of where: because if they were found inside the spike of SARS-CoV-2 it wouldn't have the same significance, but instead they are all along the external surface, a more functional area, strategically placed in one of the attack sections cited above, the *Receptor Binding Domain*. Precisely this positioning, Dalgleish and his team tell us, seems to grant the virus a superior level of pathologic aggressiveness, because it allows it to use those inserted amino acids with positive charges to create openings into the negatively-charge membranes of our cells, even in the absence of the locks, the previously discussed ACE2 receptors. This appears to be the most plausible explanation for Covid-19's ability to attack such disparate human organs, beyond the usual lungs, which are the point of entry. (ibidem) It's no coincidence that the medical nightmare that has overwhelmed, and continues to overwhelm, our hospitals was precisely the multiplicity of pathologies revealed in patients, struck with venous thrombosis, ischaemia, cardiopathies, diarrhoea, depression, chronic fatigue, loss of taste and smell, neuropathies, in addition to the acute respiratory disease at the beginning of the infection.

And now I've come to the end of the warm-up. There remains one last mystery around which to wrap your heads. It concerns the so-called "natural father" of SARS-CoV-2, the coronavirus labeled RATG13. A substantial part of the international scientific community and practically all of the mainstream media – with several authoritative exceptions, one should note – today passively accepts RATG13 as the natural ancestor to SARS-CoV-2 . However, over this supposed forefather, and even over its real existence, hangs a disconcerting scientific cloud. The plot thickens here, but I insist that the readers follow it, because if there was a response the TV-virologists brandished like a sword in order to silence any doubts on the origins of Covd-19, it was that today science knew with certainty its natural *genetic father,* RATG13. Nonsense. And what's more, this phantomlike RATG13 coronavirus also points in a truly controversial direction, to a dark world of military technology and illegal experiments which I'll only touch upon in brief.

First of all, let's take a look at the acronym. RA stands for Rhinolophus Affinis, which is an Asian bat of the Rhinolophidae family, in whose blood the virus lives. TG is more interesting, unfortunately, because it's the abbreviation of Tongguan, where the first biological sample containing this microbe was collected by scientists of the Wuhan Institute of Virology (WIV) after the sudden and mysterious death in 2012 of three people who were working in an abandoned mine full of bats in the region of Mojiang located in Yunnan province. Last, 13 refers to the year that the sample was collected, in 2013, by a team led by our *Batwoman*, Dr. Zheng-Li Shi from the WIV. The first stone against the paper scaffolding that describes SARS-CoV-2 as originating from RATG13 was immediately thrown by various scientific commentators in 2020: they pointed out that the province of Yunnan, which contains that fateful mine, is located at a distance of 1,880 kilometers from Wuhan where the pandemic exploded in 2019. Logically, the contagion would have first had to attack the population living in the Yunnan countryside which is crawling with that kind of bat, and not such a distant modern metropolis. Secondly, it was observed that, in the period of the year in which the virus was presumed to have made the recent jump from a different species in order to become SARS-CoV-2, the Rhinolophus affinis does not even fly, because it's asleep, in hibernation. (83)

But the avalanche of data that definitively discredited the hypothesis of a natural origin unleashed by RATG13 is much more extreme than that. Here is the first part: it's known that the molecular similarity between the presumed father (RATG13) and the son (SARS-CoV-2) is 96.2%, which to a layman sounds like they are nearly identical, consequentially it seems plausible for them to be related. But not at all, in fact it's the opposite. One of the most renowned evolutionary virologists, Prof Edward Holmes from the University of Sydney, was draconian on this point, along with various other international colleagues, explaining that the difference of 3.8% between the two translated to 1,200 different nucleotides, which, in turn, in evolutionary virology translates to around 50 years in generational distance – much more than the mere seven years that passed from the presumed first infection in Mojian to Covid-19's *patient zero* in China. (84)

The second side of this avalanche unfurls in the following manner: RATG13 exists only as a genetic sequence on a WIV computer, which is to say it doesn't exist *in vitro* nor *in vivo*, not even as an RNA fragment in a laboratory sample that could have been impartially examined by international experts. This is because Zheng-Li Shi said that the biological sample from which it was reconstructed was used up and that nothing was left *("there was no more sample after we finished genome sequencing")*, before openly admitting that effectively this so-called parent to SARS-CoV-2 was never physically isolated, meaning no one on earth ever saw it whole in nature. (85) The cherry on top is that its supposed striking discovery was inexplicably kept in the background by the WIV for a good seven years (except for 2 very partial citations), until – surprise, surprise – February 2020 when China was in a state of panic trying to explain to the world where this viral calamity had come from. Only at that point did Zheng-Li Shi inform her international colleagues about RATG13, with a piece published in Nature. (86) All of this doesn't make sense. I'll remind our readers that RATG13 was one of eight coronaviruses suspected of suddenly killing three workers in Mojiang through an extremely rare form of contagion that passed directly from bats to humans without any intermediate species*.

A precedent for this kind of implacable direct infection existed and was well-known to Zheng-Li Shi – I'm talking about the deadly avian influenza H5N1 which kills 60% of those infected, when in very particular conditions an enormous viral load manages to penetrate human lungs. In theory, therefore, already in 2013 RATG13 could have been a new killer with future

*Note: To avoid creating confusion for our readers I'll specify that this supposed direct contagion in 2012 in Mojiang does not contradict the idea by which the passage of a virus from an animal to humans necessitates a long period of adaptation. The reason why that extremely rare case of direct bat-to-human infection took place in a short amount of time can be found in the enormous viral load contained in the faeces of the bats continually inhaled by those workers for days on end and which is impossible to suppose in occasional infections between an animal and a human. In fact, those unlucky victims did not infect any of their family members or the hospital workers, precisely because the virus had still not adapted to infect human beings when transmitted via regular aerosols.

pandemic possibilities among the deadliest in history, and wasn't it precisely our *Batwoman* that had previously affirmed that, given the fact that two very dangerous coronaviruses – SARS and MERS – originated in bats, a great deal of attention must be given to these coronavirus lineages from bats? So, why did the scientists in Wuhan stall for years before making RATG13 fully known to the world?

A response that is likely to meet all of the parameters of logic, sense and authoritativeness is out there. It's written in a USA State Department report from January 15, 2021, titled *Fact Sheet: Activity at the Wuhan Institute of Virology* (WIV). The document states without any doubt the following: *"Despite the WIV presenting itself as a civilian institution, the United States has determined that the WIV has collaborated on publications and secret projects with China's military. The WIV has engaged in classified research, including laboratory animal experiments, on behalf of the Chinese military since at least 2017."* (87) This is very possibly why *Batwoman* had to stay quiet about the startling discovery of the so-called *father* of SARS-CoV-2, which would have been of urgent interest for public health. The US document cites clearly intense experiments on the coronavirus RATG13 that Zheng-Li Shi had conducted from 2016, accusing her and her Institute of not being *"transparent or consistent about its record of studying viruses most similar to the Covid-19 virus"* – exactly (ibidem). Finally, it reveals to us the cover-up of a disconcerting fact: *"The U.S. government has reason to believe that several researchers inside the WIV became sick in autumn 2019, before the first identified case of the outbreak, with symptoms consistent with both Covid-19 and common seasonal illnesses. This raises questions about the credibility of WIV senior researcher Shi Zheng-Li's public claim that there was 'zero infection' among the WIV's staff and students of SARS-CoV-2 or SARS-related viruses."* (ibidem)

The illness that these Chinese scientist caught, at the Wuhan Institute of all places, required immediate hospitalization, with serious conditions, and happened in the ark of a single week as revealed, citing *"some high end information collected by our intelligence community, only a swath of which was declassified"*, by the former special consultant of the State Department David Asher in a seminar on March 17, 2021. [88] It wasn't a flu.

And so, if considered in light of the closeness between the Beijing army and the Wuhan Institute of Virology, of which US Intelligence has proof, the "familial" relationship between RATG13 and SARS-CoV-2 does in fact become plausible –just as long as the adjective "natural" is taken out, and then everything fits together.

I will stop here. Angus Dalgleish and Steven Quay will now draw from their internationally recognised and vast scientific background to present further, and in depth, molecular evidence to paint the true picture of this pandemic virus as it was originally manufactured to make it capable of attacking so many different cell classes, thus human organs, in the context of the most extreme form of virological research: Gain of Function.

Is Anything Else Really Necessary?

That which I have presented up to this point does not claim to be in any way exhaustive. For example, referring back to what has just been documented above, I did not expand upon the concrete interferences that the Chinese secret service and military apparatus manifestly carried out in the work of the Wuhan Institute of Biological Products and of the National Engineering Technology Research Center for Combined Vaccines, contiguous entities to the army of the Chinese Communist Party which, however, had heavily involved Zheng-Li Shi's Wuhan Institute of Virology. Their common denominator was the study and the manipulation of SARS-related coronaviruses, right up to the start of the pandemic. Authoritative sources of international intelligence have already dealt with the mingling of Beijing's Defence and the biotechnical research in Wuhan, particularly in relation to Covid-19. (89) The reason why I'll stop here and give the floor to the book's scientific co-authors is precisely that, in my opinion, the pieces of molecular and factual evidence synthesized thus far, which will be added to and looked at in further detail in the rest of this volume, are by this point sufficiently overwhelming to incite both the general public as well as experts, and above all politicians, to exclaim *"Is anything else really necessary"* to finally demand that the full truth about this virus and the deadly omissions that accompanied its outbreak be spoken by the Chinese scientists and by their backers in the United States?

China has been lying to its citizens and to the world since January 2020 and it should be backed into a corner with the overflowing evidence, so that the international scientific community can be free to delve into every meaningful detail on how the worst pandemic in a century unfolded, in order to pursue the vital goal of really effective treatments and lasting vaccines. It's up to public opinion to stop geopolitics and big business from getting in the way, accepting the high price of truth at various levels without which Covid-19 will still not be easy to abate. Furthermore, and this is no less central, the countdown to the next pandemic – the next body bags, the next lockdowns, and the next trillions of dollars in planetary damages – has already started some time ago in the Gain of Function of concern laboratories scattered throughout the world. It's a debate that should be urgently brought into the foreground, unless we want to relive everything from the start, and probably much worse.

Lastly I want, I must, reiterate something that has been spelt out more than once in these pages, and that is how the collusions, the conspiracy of silence, the scientific red herrings pedalled by some Chinese scientists and bureaucrats under the yoke of Beijing and abetted by sections of Western science in the pay of a political crusade cost humanity scores of innocent lives that could otherwise still be here with us. This is, in my opinion, the worst of the many scandals of the Covid-19 pandemic.

Acknowledgements

A special thanks to: Dr Michael Antoniou, geneticist at King's College London and one of the pioneers among the sceptics of the zoonotic origin; Elizabeth Thomson and Anthony Filby in London for early consultancy; Dr Massimo Fazzari and environmentalist Nicolas Micheletti in Italy for their cooperation; the Professors Simon Wain-Hobson (Pasteur Institute, Paris), David Walt (Harvard University), David Relman (Stanford University), Marc Lipsitch (Harvard T.H. Chan School of Public Health), Donald K. Milton (University of Maryland), and John Ioannidis (Stanford University) for their scientific advise. A thought for my mother who introduced me to the love of the sciences and infinite gratitude to my wife Danielle for looking after my mental sanity as I struggled to put together this book.

*Chimeric Chameleon**
by Prof. Angus Dalgleish

Background to getting involved with Covid-19 research.

The story of how I got involved in identifying how this virus was far from natural has intrigued many as I am a clinician specialising in cancer medicine. However, this disguises the fact that after fully qualifying as a consultant medical oncologist and gaining the Fellowship of the Royal Australian College of Physicians (FRACP) I decided to pursue a research degree in Human Retroviruses, having previously declined the opportunity to do so. My training in oncology, at the Royal Prince Alfred Hospital and Royal North Shore Hospital Sydney, had exposed me to the potential of viruses causing cancer and the role of the immune system in determining outcomes.

The interest in viruses and cancer came about because of the observation that many patients with primary liver cancer had no history of alcohol abuse, as I had been taught. At that time, reports were appearing of a link to the newly discovered Hepatitis B virus (HBV) and liver cancer. The recent ability to measure the antibodies gave me the tools to show that over 98% of all primary liver cancers diagnosed in Sydney were HBV positive. Also, at this time, patients were presenting with unusual infections and lymphomas, a clinical syndrome which was later to be recognised as AIDS. We noted that early Australian patients had all visited San Francisco, where the first cases were reported.

This further enhanced my desire to do research into viruses, the immune system and cancer. I was accepted as a clinical

* The adjective chimeric in the title refers to the scientific term chimera that defines a laboratory engineered pathogen. The Chimeric Chameleon thus alludes to Covid-19 being a manipulated virus disguised as natural.

research fellow by Professor Robin Weiss at the Institute of Cancer Research, London, and started to research the first human retroviruses, such as the HTLV-1. I was inducted into laboratory techniques to try to discover the cell receptor for HTLV-1 when the viruses (known as LAV and HTLV-III) became available from Luc Montagnier and Robert Gallo. This led to the pursuit of what would be required to develop an ideal HIV vaccine, which in turn led to a collaboration with Birger Sørensen and BionorPharma in Norway. Birger had already identified four unique epitopes for an AIDS vaccine, known as Vacc4X, which was to show a significant reduction in viral load in a randomised trial in HIV positive patients. However, it did not lead to a significant rise in CD4 levels, which was an endpoint, that is, a necessary condition for the development of a successful vaccine against HIV. My research in the field of infectious disease and molecular biology continued with a number of discoveries that cemented my collaboration with Birger.

Now fast forward several years: it was against this distant background that at the outbreak of the 2020 pandemic Birger called to see if I would be interested in developing a Covid-19 vaccine. I was excited by this new challenge as I suggested to him that a SARS-CoV-2 vaccine may benefit from an even better adjuvant than we had used previously. In fact, in my research work as a clinical oncologist I had noted that a laboratory product (IMM-101) used to enhance the innate immune response in cancer patients appeared to protect them from viral infections as well, especially seasonal flu and colds. This bode well for a vaccine against the new infectious killer that just in those weeks was beginning to ravage Europe having emerged in Wuhan, China, apparently only a short time before. As soon as the sequence for SARS-CoV-2 became available, Birger, his team and I started intense work on it, but it was at this point, as it often happens in scientific research, that we stumbled into a number of findings that were decisively at odds with the mainstream narrative on the natural origin of Covid-19, also called zoonosis. They could not be ignored, and we didn't, till our own research uncovered what we consider unmistakable evidence not just of the obvious laboratory origin of the present pandemic virus, but also of the degree of manipulation it underwent and of its thus far undisclosed lethal features, which forms our signature contribution to this crucial inquest into what really happened to the most deadly virus in a century.

Unexpected Findings

This virus appeared at once to us as highly uncharacteristic for a coronavirus closely related to the SARS family. One fact that particularly drew the attention of Birger and I was that its Spike Proteins have inserted sequences which are structurally similar to other types of Spikes found on the surface of the HIV virus, that causes AIDS. How can this have happened in a bat coronavirus that is so distant from the HIV retrovirus? It is important to be aware that HIV proviruses were used in 2010 by Zheng-Li Shi and her colleagues at the Wuhan laboratories in experiments aiming at selecting among bat coronaviruses those that learnt to best infect human cells through the ACE-2 receptors, a feature that closely suggests other isolates were part of the Gain of Function (GOF) experiments at the WIV. Records show that the team were aware of the 'risks' of this type of research, using viruses with high infectivity of human respiratory cells.[(1)] In addition, as previously explained in this book, SARS-CoV-2 contains a *Furin Cleavage Site*, absent in coronaviruses of the same family and strongly suggestive of more GOF interference in this pandemic killer.

However, GOF research popped once more into the frame we were observing. As it's sadly known by now, Covid-19 has taken the medical world by storm with its shocking ability to infect so many different classes of human cells. This book has already explained that this nefarious ability is bestowed on a virus by the power of its Spike Proteins, whose building blocks are called amino acids. The more powerful the Spike Proteins, the more devastating the virus will be on human organisms. Theoretically nature can "weaponize" a Spike to that effect, however scientists can also purposely make a Spike Protein super aggressive in unlocking the ACE2 receptors on human cells by altering its amino acids. This is precisely what coronavirus Gain of Function (GOF) research has learnt how to do. A major 2007 study by Wuze Ren et al can be used here to efficaciously illustrate how GOF works in this case. They experimented on both the 2003 SARS coronavirus and a SARS-like coronavirus of bat origin, acronym SL-CoV. The former was notoriously able to bind to our ACE2 receptors and thus infect us, the latter could not. By operating a minimal modification in the amino acids of the Spike Protein belonging to the harmless SL-CoV, Wuze Ren and his colleagues were able to convert it from non-ACE2 binding to human ACE2 binding, thus turning this harmless coronavirus into a potential human pathogen.(2) And here we circle back to Gain of Function because experiments of this kind are at the moment the only plausible explanation for Covid-19's shocking ability to make humans sick in so many ways.

I wish to stress that it is not possible to analyse a number of further anomalies of SARS-CoV-2 – which Sørensen and I specifically highlighted in our research and form the core of our chapter – without considering that there are several laboratories within the Wuhan Institute of Virology involved in GOF research.

We now wish to share a very brief comment on Gain of Function because we truly believe that the experiments being conducted under the aegis of this scientific field and of its mentors could be humanity's shortest and surest way to relive the tragedy of Covid-19 all over again and possibly even worse.

Why is such dangerous research being pursued?

The reason given for undertaking Gain of Function (GOF) studies is in order to find out which viruses are likely to be a future hazard to human beings and to develop vaccines and treatments before the viruses become a problem. This reasoning is flawed. In GOF work to make a virus pathogenic it is necessary to pass it through *chimeric* animals such as humanized mice, to add Spike Proteins from another totally different species of virus, to genetically engineer the virus in ways that are never found in nature. Thus GOF experiments create pathogens using technology and artificial passaging through cells they would never normally encounter to make a 'unique' pathogen that would never evolve to that extent naturally and hence would never be a problem in the first place.

There are millions of unknown viruses in every gallon of sea water. Studying them all with GOF studies would simply result in millions more diseases that are untreatable and would solve nothing, and that's just the sea water.

When this type of research is explained to working doctors whose mission is to cure diseases, the medical practitioners are speechless. The obvious folly of making another, as yet untreatable disease does not escape them. Medical science is extremely complex and astonishing advances have been made but making another disease just in case it might sometime exist is sheer madness.

There is, of course, the possibility that such studies have been undertaken for malign reasons and that there was no benign intent in the first place. The Wuhan Institute of Virology has been taken over by the Chinese military and the place is now being run by the top bio-weapons expert in China. It makes one think.

Instead of calling the experiments Gain of Function (GOF) studies it would be better to call them what they are. Stop sweetening the pill, simply call them Make Another Disease (MAD) experiments being carried out by 'MAD' scientists.

If GOF research were only going to cause monster viruses that could only impact cells and mice and never escape then a case could be made that it does not matter to anyone but the scientists concerned. However, the claim that this research is only carried out in laboratories which are safe, and from which such leaks are impossible, is sadly deluded. China has consistently insisted that all such research has been conducted in Biosafety Level 4 laboratories where it is theoretically impossible for any escape to occur whatsoever and even the laboratory operatives are 100% cocooned in protective suits.

However, even if this was so, dangerous pathogens have escaped from even the most safe containment facilities at times. This because no human system will ever be able to predict, account for and bring under control the usual universal law of human incompetence (think Chernobyl). One glaring example of it was the outbreak of the 'Foot and Mouth Disease' while it was being researched in the safest facility in the U.K. (so it was claimed) and which was in splendid isolation. However, this did not prevent an accident which resulted in the escape of the Foot and Mouth virus and which led to the slaughter of seven million cows, the destruction of thousands of farms and their associated businesses, and the suicide out of utter despair of hundreds of farmers. This completely safe facility suddenly became a biological hazard, leading to an epidemic of death and destruction of cattle of dystopian proportions. In fact it was a plumber called in to attend to the toilets who inappropriately undid the wrong pipe that allowed out the highly infectious agent to spill on the ground (soil) where it slowly seeped down an embankment onto a lane where it was picked up by a passing tractor tyre, which contaminated the first farm. The traditional movement of livestock meant that it was quickly spread around the country. If this is what occurs in a completely guaranteed safe laboratory, what hope for the others? We know that Biosafety Level 2 or 3 laboratories where the majority of pathogens are researched have a consistent record of leaks, most of which go unreported outside of the Institutes.

We now know that much of the GOF work on the coronaviruses in Wuhan were conducted in Biosafety Level 2 laboratories, which means that a 'leak' should have been expected, even in the most stringent conditions. However, such conditions were not kept as the 2018 inspection of the Wuhan labs found. They were not operated at the standards expected elsewhere and the conduct and adherence to operating procedures fell way below that which the NIH would have expected from a laboratory working on easily transmitted pathogens.

Now consider that the WHO special mission to determine the origins of Covid-19 concluded that leaks were so unlikely that they could be written off as a source! Many scientists are, however, aware of the fact that this is simply untrue and that lab leaks are a remarkably common event and have resulted in dire consequences on a worrying number of occasions in the past. If that was the only reason for discarding the lab-leak theory it was clearly unconvincing. Coupled with the fact that the WHO team did not inspect the laboratories or even have access to the laboratory records it is no wonder the WHO report resulted in concern on the part of politicians and scientists who might previously have preferred the zoonosis theory despite the lack of evidence for it.

It should be very clear by now that the risk of a dangerous pathogen, whether natural or selected by GOF studies, leaking out and causing a pandemic is not low but, relative to the damage caused, extremely high.

The Wuhan Institute of Virology contains over 600 coronavirus specimens, which could escape at any time and it is not the only laboratory of concern both in China and in the world. There are extremely dangerous pathogens which if they escaped and got a hold in a community could cause even worse damage than Covid-19. Simon Wain-Hobson, the eminent Pasteur Institute virologist, has already claimed that it would be possible to make HIV-1 airborne transmissible, and this is an agent against which, after thirty years, we still have no effective vaccine!

A long-ago retired director of Porton Down, one of the most secretive military research facilities in the U.K., told his nephew on a visit that he should not be concerned about nuclear weapons, in the future it is the potential of microbiological organisms to escape that is the real threat to humanity. How true his concerns have proved.

What the papers said...

Bearing this in mind, and as an introduction to the following scientific analysis of the real background story of Covid-19, it is worth reviewing a sequence of GOF research papers, which I believe will not only greatly enhance public understanding of how misleading was the natural zoonotic hypothesis for this virus, but it will also give a sense of the GOF "slippery slope" as it still is today.

A substantial amount of GOF research has been undertaken on the SARS-Coronaviruses but four studies are especially noteworthy. They are linked in two ways. Scientifically, in that the third and fourth build upon the results of the first and second; and in the continuity of the institution and personnel involved: The Wuhan Institute of Virology is a key collaborator in these projects and Dr Zheng-Li Shi, one of the most senior and experienced of the Institute's virologists and bat specialists, appears in some capacity in all of them. What follows may appear at first foggy to you, but bear with me and it will become clear at the end.

1. In 2010 scientists from the 'Special Viruses' section of the Wuhan Institute of Virology were engaged in Gain of Function experiments, jointly with international collaborators, to increase coronaviruses infectiousness for humans. What they did was, to put it simply, to play about with bat and human ACE2 receptors in order to better train some SARS-like coronaviruses to efficaciously infect the latter, us humans that is.

2. In 2015 scientists from the same 'Special Viruses' section of the Wuhan Institute of Virology were still engaged in Gain of Function work with a team from the University of North Carolina Chapel Hill. Together, they manipulated bat viruses to create a *chimera,* that is, an artificial man-made virus, called SHC014-MA15 which binds to and can proliferate on human upper airway cells. The lead Wuhan scientist, who provided the coronavirus material, was Dr Zheng-Li Shi. We note that what is described here are, in fact, what today the entire world would instantly recognize as Covid-19 properties. In fact *in vivo* experiments at Chapel Hill replicated the *chimeric virus* in mice lungs which showed significant pathogenesis, which was the opposite of what the team had expected but just like the present SARS-CoV-2 virus. We can see, therefore, that the 2015 experiment advanced the 2010 work by perfecting in animal trials a virus optimised to infect the human upper respiratory tract. The 2015 authors were well aware that the *chimeric* virus which they had created was very dangerous because they discussed this fact. They also speculated that *"review panels may deem similar studies too risky to pursue as increased pathogenicity in mammalian models cannot be excluded."* It is certainly the case that this experiment created a *chimeric* virus with very high infectivity and it

was potentially targeted to the human upper respiratory tract. We deduce from the paper's authorships that this was done in the Wuhan Institute of Virology.

3. In 2018 Zhou P. et.al, investigated a coronavirus outbreak associated with a fatal Swine Acute Diarrhea Syndrome (SADS) in Guangdong Province (an epidemic in pigs).(3) In sum, what this paper showed us is that this coronavirus used none of the three receptors it was expected to latch onto including the well known ACE2 and was clearly utilizing different entry into the cells. At that point the scientists decided to dig into the pigs' cells to discover which receptors the SADS coronavirus was using by "digging them up" as it were. They demonstrated considerable skills in this "hunt" for receptors and in testing them against a dangerous coronavirus.

4. Finally, the fourth publication of interest. In 2015 Workman et.al, discussed bitter/sweet taste receptors and the role these receptors play in mediating airway immune functions.(4) They summarised their results thus: "*Over the past several years, taste receptors have emerged as key players in the regulation of innate immune defenses in the mammalian respiratory tract.*"

So, let's finally collect our thoughts. These four publications take us through a Gain of Function journey that starts in 2010 with Wuhan researchers perfecting their ability to make coronaviruses infect human cells. Then in 2015 other scientists developed a highly infectious chimeric virus especially capable of infecting the human upper respiratory tract. In 2018 yet another team demonstrated skills in searching for the all important receptors for coronavirus infections when said virus bypassed the classic

ACE2 receptor. Lastly, three years earlier more researchers told us that the receptors on human cells responsible for taste play important roles in activating our immune response in the respiratory tract.

Now, Covid-19's action on humans seems to be the exact result of these four laboratory works: SARS-CoV-2 is a coronavirus that has learned to infect human cells – as in the 2010 and in particular the 2015 experiments. SARS-CoV-2 seems to be capable of attacking cells with no ACE2 receptors and this ability could have been conferred to it through knowledge and techniques acquired in a lab – the 2018 experiment; SARS-CoV-2 causes massive respiratory damage by precisely disabling the cells responsible for taste in humans which are key to the activation of our respiratory immune response – the second 2015 experiment. And precisely this indicates in my opinion that the 2019 pandemic virus comes from the 2015 chimeric virus that has been purposely optimized to disable our taste and thus our airways immunity.

All this explains the otherwise puzzling extreme infectivity of SARS-CoV-2 and hence also the social epidemiology of its spread. It should not escape readers that both the Wuhan Institute of Virology and its leading researcher Dr Zheng-Li Shi were pervasive in this sequence of events.

Analysis of the viral genome and the charge on the Spike Proteins. The signature contribution of Dalgleish and Sørensen to this inquest

In February 2020 Birger Sørensen modelled the genome and Spike Proteins of SARS-CoV-2 using the published data which had been leaked to the world by a Wuhan virologist. A quick literature search revealed numerous references by Zheng-Li

Shi regarding the Gain of Function studies and, in light of the peculiar nature of the additional positive electric charge in the SARS-CoV-2 Spike Proteins that Sørensen and I discovered, we proposed that the novel 2019 coronavirus had been created from a bat coronavirus by laboratory insertions of amino acids in its Spike Protein, which in fact are clearly present in the structure of SARS-CoV-2.[5] Do keep in mind the "additional positive electric charge" I just mentioned, as it plays a key role in this virus's deadly infectivity.

Some of these insertions were identified by unusual AA sequences, where AA simply means amino acids. The amino acid of interest here is called *Arginine* because it was discovered that the "genetic instructions" which "built" *Arginine* in the SARS-CoV-2 Spike Proteins are not found in any other coronavirus of its family. This is again highly suspicious, like the rest of the peculiarities this virus has and which are nowhere to be found in nature.

This assumes particular importance as the additional positive electric charge associated with these sequences (insertions) seem to be what enables SARS-CoV-2 Spikes to attach to the negatively charged cell membranes via the so called extra-*Arginine* "bridges", allowing it to bypass in some instances its usual route of infection that would require locking onto the specific ACE2 receptors on the surface of the human cell. You will have understood that most viruses use a very specific receptor, like a unique key for a lock, but taken together these sequences, and the additional positive electric charge they are endowed with, *can act like a master key and enter negatively charged cells' surfaces without a perfect specific receptor*. This is pivotal in explaining the devastating ability of SARS-CoV-2 to infect so many different human organs.

Now, here is the crucial question: how did this pandemic coronavirus "arm" its Spike Proteins with these unusual insertions and additional positive electric charge? The very fact that no other member of its family possesses them is strongly indicative of a laboratory manipulation, in fact Gain of Function research uses precisely these "tricks" to make an animal pathogen infectious for humans.

Every single charged AA sequence can make a difference in the aggressiveness of SARS-CoV-2 as the clinical manifestations of the disease and the Long Covid syndrome in recovered patients demonstrate. A brief overview of them will give the reader a sense of the extreme pathogenicity of SARS-CoV-2 in the precise context of the two discoveries that we made. This pandemic is associated with a broad range of clinical manifestations, many of which involve symptoms, and affect cells, suggesting the use of receptors other than ACE2 via the extra-*Arginine* "bridges" mentioned before. For instance, the loss of smell and taste suggests direct invasion of taste and smell bitter/sweet receptors. The virus can destroy erythrocytes and hence their ability to carry oxygen, leading to the classic shortness of breath requiring oxygen administration. In addition, the important cells of the immune system (lymphocytes) are attacked, which contributes to the immunological chaos and inflammatory response, which is the prelude to death from Covid-19. The additional effect on clotting pathways, which leads to clots and inflammation in the lungs, also contribute to this. Moreover, it would now appear that any cell can be affected, either by direct infection or indirectly by the clotting and inflammatory processes induced, which can lead to cardiac failure, vasculitis (anywhere) and kidney failure.

Additionally of concern are the neurological manifestations, which often cause severe headache, confusion and fatigue. The encephalitis caused is expressed by severe cognitive deficiencies and confusion, often referred to as 'brain fog'. This is a major worry as it can linger for many months and together with fatigue and shortness of breath lead to what is commonly referred to as Long Covid. This condition is so bad that it leads to the infected person being unable to function and return to work, even finding difficulty in sleeping, getting out of bed and especially getting up the stairs, even if they do manage to leave the bedroom.

Another manifestation is severe muscle pain and weakness, which prevents many day-to-day functions from being performed. I have reviewed several such patients who still have these symptoms preventing them from working or studying six-twelve months on from a positive Covid-19 test acute infection. They report the classic symptoms of sore throat, cough, fever, shortness of breath and loss of smell and taste. These Long Covid cases are all SARS-CoV-2 antigen (PCR) test negative, meaning that the original infection has cleared, but show classic antibodies. These clinical manifestations are similar to the Chronic Fatigue Syndrome (~CFS) that can occur after Epstein Barr Virus (EBV) infection. Unfortunately, there is no known curative agent, in spite of many agents being tried. The overall condition would appear to be a chronic inflammatory one which would make it an indirect manifestation of acute Covid-19 infection and which continues long after the virus has cleared. In the case of EBV associated CFS the virus is still present, having become a chronic infection.

Let me now remind the readers of the pivotal point here: this tragic state of affairs is precisely correlated with the above-mentioned discovery of the unusual AAs insertions and their added positive charge in the SARS-CoV-2 Spike Proteins that no other coronavirus of this class possesses, but which are instead signature traits of Gain of Function work. In fact the enhanced presence of AAs has been noted to enhance pathogenicity in other microbes, such as the 1997 H7N1 Hong Kong flu. In addition, one should remember the aforementioned presence in the SARS-CoV-2 Spike Proteins of inserts homologous to components of the HIV virus and these too enable extra-*Arginine* "bridges" to attach to the membranes of human cells without the use of specific ACE receptors.

The bottom line is that many of these symptoms cannot be explained by cells expressing the ACE2 receptors as the mainstream theory maintains, suggesting that other cell types can be directly infected and here our above-mentioned discoveries play a crucial role as well as pointing again to Gain of Function work.

So to simplify the molecular traits Sørensen and I have discovered in our research work on the origins of Covid-19 let me recap:

Firstly, there are at least three major receptor mechanisms of entry which are relevant in the case of SARS-CoV-2 and not just the ACE2 receptor. For example the virus is able to use receptors such as the DC-SIGN/CLEC4M.

Secondly, as this book has already detailed, the ACE2 receptor binding is supremely well adapted, which would be unlikely if this virus had had a zoonotic origin but is quite possible if one contemplates human hand intervention through the intensive Gain of Function studies previously performed to optimize ACE2 receptor binding.

Thirdly, the SARS-CoV-2 Spike Protein has clear evidence of inserts containing amino acids like *Arginine* which were "built" with highly unusual "instructions" for coronaviruses and which have been associated with enhance pathogenicity in other pathogens, such as the 1997 H7N1 Hong Kong flu. In addition these inserts carry positive additional charges that, together with inserts homologous to components of the HIV virus, enable SARS-CoV-2 to latch onto negatively charged human cells' membranes via the so called extra-*Arginine* "bridges" entirely bypassing the use of specific ACE receptors. In conclusion, these SARS-COV-2 Spike Proteins have a very high charge with an isoelectric point of 8.24 compared with only 5.67 for the 2003 SARS Spike Proteins. This extra electric charge could explain the extreme pathogenicity seen with Covid-19.

These powerful traits are extremely unlikely to have evolved naturally as they appear to be unique in Covid-19 as opposed to all the coronavirus strains prior to the 2019 outbreak that have been analysed, even though they are otherwise very similar to each other. On the other hand scientific records show that they are common features of laboratory experiments with Gain of Function.

Why has the debate been stymied and the investigation so delayed?

The discussion about the origin of the virus has been unfairly presented and the lab-leak theory dismissed until very recently. It is our contention that this censorship of scientific debate has harmed the entire process and advancement of science and held back the very necessary fight against the pandemic.

Back in February of 2020 when Daszak masterminded an orchestrated letter in *The Lancet* he cannot have had any specific knowledge to suggest that Covid-19 did not arise from a laboratory leak because he had done no investigation. He disingenuously cajoled other scientists to sign the letter without disclosure of the fact that experiments producing very similar *chimeric* – that is, genetically manipulated - coronaviruses had indeed been carried out at the facilities in Wuhan.

Daszak was himself a co-author on many of the papers and presentations that were in complete contradiction to the assertion in *The Lancet* letter. Daszak (in an interview with the media) has since admitted that the letter was written in order to protect the Chinese virologists. The effect of such publications in early 2020 was to make a pariah of anybody who suggested that the virus did originate from one of the three virology laboratories in Wuhan. Immediately they were dismissed as peddlers of conspiracy theories and racist cranks. Even scientists of high repute found that any articles they produced were turned down by journals and newspapers if they suggested that the laboratory origin theory should be entertained. YouTube and Facebook censored social media posts that referred to a laboratory origin and have only very recently stated that they will reverse that policy.

We wish to stress that the frantic response to anyone (especially the scientific co-authors in this book) that suggested that the unexpected inserts in this virus were more likely to have come from GOF studies in Wuhan than from natural evolution was unprecedented in virological research. It now appears that the head of the Welcome Trust, Sir Jeremy Farrar and the UK Chief Scientific Officer, Sir Patrick Vallance, had secret communications with the head of the NIAID (National Institutes of Health), Dr Anthony Fauci, precisely about the presence of unnatural inserts in the SARS-CoV-2 virus. This has all been revealed in a series of explosive emails made available through freedom of information legislation in the U.S. Following this, Dr Fauci gave his backing to Daszak and colleagues in communicating that it was a natural virus and that there was no evidence of a lab origin when all of them harboured at least a suspicion.

Why was this not openly debated and why were papers from authors in this book, who tried to highlight the evidence, prevented from being published in any journal, all of whom returned such papers as *'not in the public interest'* ?

Bayesian deduction and Occam's razor made the lab-leak theory far more likely than a zoonotic natural infection. So why did they cover it up? Why did the WHO lie? And why did millions have to die? Unless this is answered it is certain to be repeated again and again.

Let's now try to entertain at least the main reasons why the scientific community refused to even countenance the thought that the SARS-CoV-2 was anything but a naturally evolved wild virus.

The paper that completely disagreed with its conclusions. One publication that carried a lot of weight among those striving to muffle the origins debate was authored by Kristian Andersen et al in *Nature Medicine* and it stated unequivocally that *"It is improbable that SARS-CoV-2 emerged through laboratory manipulation of a related SARS-CoV-like coronavirus."* [6] However no reason was given for this assertion except that a computer analysis had suggested that though the SARS-CoV-2 may bind human ACE2 with high affinity the interaction was not ideal. However, paradoxically, the study would also state that previous experiments with the 2003 SARS coronavirus had shown that *"[laboratory] insertion of a Furin Cleavage Site at the S1–S2 junction enhances cell–cell fusion"*. Why is this significant? The author reminded us, blatantly contradicting himself, that a Gain of Function experiment on the 2003 SARS coronavirus had produced precisely a virus which *"emerged through laboratory manipulation of a related SARS-CoV-like coronavirus"* with enhanced powers. How could then Andersen, of all scientists, categorically exclude that SARS-CoV-2 may have been created in exactly this way? Surely his own paper supports at the very least the possibility that such laboratory Gain of Function work may have also interfered with SARS-CoV-2.

Indeed research published from 2015 to 2018 shows that the team of scientists in Wuhan did add Spike Proteins to coronaviruses and this had made them more infective.[7] Here is a direct quote from a paper in 2015 *"Therefore, to examine the emergence potential (that is, the potential to infect humans) of circulating bat CoVs, we built a chimeric virus encoding a novel, zoonotic CoV Spike Protein"*. It is interesting that years later, after the outbreak of the pandemic, the online editors of this study felt it was necessary to add the following statement to the 2015 paper: *"Editors' note, March 2020: We are aware that this article is being used as the basis for unverified theories that the novel coronavirus causing Covid-19 was engineered. There is no evidence that this is true; scientists believe that an animal is the most likely source of the coronavirus."*

How intriguing that the editors of *Nature Medicine* feel able to speak for all scientists in that way, deriding theories based on papers published in their own journal and rubbishing the argument without providing evidence to back their statement!

Avoid offence. First and foremost was the desire, as expressed by Peter Daszak, to avoid offending or even endangering the Chinese virologists. This can be extended to a desire to avoid blaming the Chinese as a whole. It is, of course, certain that the public in Wuhan, whether in the meat market or elsewhere in the city, were victims just as much as anyone else in the world. The Chinese people should not be blamed but their government should be.

Chinese Finance. A more worrying reason is that Chinese Communist party funds are being poured into many universities in the United Kingdom and the USA via the very large number of Chinese students being paid for by the Chinese state. The Chinese government is offering huge scholarships to their citizens who are admitted to British and American universities and paying large fees to the establishments for their tuition. In addition capital funding for the universities has been forthcoming from the Chinese Communist Party.

Similarly, as previously stated in this book, some of the top scientific journals have been supported by Chinese finance. Academic institutions and publishers must grapple with the question of when engagement becomes complicity.

Avoidance of blame. Are some of the participants in virology research - American, British and Chinese - afraid that the virus did indeed originate from their experiments or from techniques they had taught other people and they would therefore be blamed for the tragedy? If they were considered to be at fault the litigation could cost them inordinate amounts of money. Supporting this contention is the way that Dr Anthony Fauci and Peter Daszak are backtracking on some of their previous pronouncements. Fauci recently claimed that the National Institutes of Health (NIH) did not fund Gain of Function (GOF) studies in Wuhan. It is a fact that he was in charge of the transfer of the funds to Daszak's EcoHealth Alliance NGO and their stated aim was to do GOF studies in Wuhan so why was he lying? Meanwhile the Chinese virologists have been removing references to GOF, NIH and Fauci from their publications.

It is also highly likely that virologists working in established laboratories outside China do not want the spotlight of suspicion turned on their own research. Although they did not create SARS-CoV-2 in their laboratories it is an established fact in microbiology that, using Gain of Function studies, they have already made other *chimeric* monsters and that some of them are likely to escape from their creators clutches as the all too real historical record of laboratory leaks suggests. Once the public realises that these laboratories, so often located in densely populated areas, are harbouring deadly diseases previously unknown to humanity they will want the process stopped and the viruses destroyed. The results of the experiments are frequently shrouded in mystery and hidden from scrutiny for commercial reasons, and the intellectual property involved is guarded by secrecy. The occasional outbreaks of novel viral diseases could turn into further pandemics and the only way to stop this is to call a total halt on the research which would then put at risks the jobs of the virologists employed at the GOF studies.

Anti-Trump sentiments. 2020 was election year in the United States and during the Covid-19 pandemic anti-Trump feelings and rhetoric were running high. When President Trump reported that the virus was the result of a laboratory experiment that had escaped control the people who did not like Trump instantly assumed that he was wrong. The more times he called it "the Chinese Virus" the greater their 'default' antagonism to the idea became. The forum to question the origin of the virus only opened up when President Biden looked at the evidence and concluded that more investigation was necessary. The debate should have occurred early in 2020 but the subject had become politicised and partisan thinking infected the response to the virus.

The politicization of the origin of SARS-CoV-2 has led the world to pay a very high price indeed for what must be the most non-scientific response to a suggestion ever. Trump had clearly seen classified documents suggesting the possibility that this virus could have escaped from a Wuhan lab and that it could have been associated with GOF experiments, the same evidence Biden was shown after his election. Indeed, two Nobel laureates have been on record, at different times, stating that the virus had very unusual sequences, with Luc Montagnier noting that it was no natural pathogen and David Baltimore referring to the *Furin Cleavage Site* as a "smoking gun". Simon Wain Hobson at the Pasteur Institute also concluded just recently that GOF isolates are very easy to make without leaving trace of the human hand. The fact that the Democrats and a few elites hated Trump and his Republican supporters meant that all of this was dismissed without inspecting the evidence and a mass lemming-like decision was made. I would argue that this is one of the biggest dereliction of scientists' duty ever. This once again goes back to the cover up by Daszak and all his colleagues and the Stockholm syndrome-like protection of China and how it had hijacked the WHO, which if they had done their duty would have taken over and greatly limited the contagion in the rest of the world. Why did they not stop international flights from Wuhan and China to the West when Wuhan was totally locked down? Why did they go along with the farcical 2021 inspection and report when all necessary evidence was withheld and all necessary visits to patients and the labs were denied?

It is clear that recent events have revealed that it was known there was something unusual about the virus on sequencing, which was recognized but apparently ignored. It would appear that all these areas of concern were explained away, one by one. The *Furin Cleavage Site* was explained away as being present on other viruses, ignoring the fact that they are not the same clade (family) as SARS-CoV-2. Inserts are not uncommon either but the SARS-CoV-2 ones have been ignored as not unexpected when it is not at all a foregone conclusion. The fact that these contain HIVgp120 sequences which are used in experiments as a retroviral vector to insert ACE2 receptors in different cells (and also to enable the extra-*Arginine* "bridges" as previously explained) was brushed over by saying they could have occurred by chance, when in fact they are well known GOF techniques and should have rung alarm bells. Similarly, the Amino Acid sequences with *Arginines* in them giving an additional positive charge to SARS-CoV-2 Spike Proteins have been dismissed as occurring in other viruses, omitting to acknowledge that they are not found in any coronavirus of the SARS-CoV-2 family.

It is clearly a fact that the sum of these changes confers supreme adaptation for infecting human cells and cannot be explained by natural evolution, especially the placement of the positive charged AA sequence located towards the cell membrane, which would explain the unique isoelectric charge of over 8, far higher than any other natural coronavirus.

The Chinese government silences all its critics and has been shown to be lying with regard to the beginning of the outbreak and to the level of person to person infectivity of the disease. The Chinese virologists would not be allowed to speak out and those who have done so are now hiding in the USA or have disappeared. Peter Daszak is a co-author and sponsor of the work that we say most likely resulted in Covid-19. Many of the virologists in the USA and elsewhere in the world are either funded by China or by the United States' National Institutes of Health (NIH) via Dr Fauci who formally green-lighted the GOF studies and via Peter Daszak who personally funnelled millions of dollars to Dr Zheng-Li Shi in Wuhan. It is not in their interest to whistle-blow about such studies and, most seriously, they have not made their conflict of interests known in any of their early publications about the Covid-19.

The former head of the Centre for Disease Control (CDC) in the US, Robert Redfield, has recently admitted that he too had became convinced that the SARS-CoV-2 virus had escaped from a Wuhan laboratory. This is a fundamental debate because Gain Of Function studies are continuing and new diseases, sometimes deadly in the extreme, are being created daily. We believe that GOF studies, which we have renamed Make Another Disease (MAD) experiments, should again be banned but this time globally. The chimeric viruses lurking in laboratory fridges, just waiting for an inadvertent power cut to let them out, should be destroyed and the commercial concerns, intellectual property rights etc. should be ignored. This is an urgent consideration.

We have presented the most unsettling facets that surrounded the tragic outbreak of Covid-19, many of them previously undisclosed to the public who urgently need to grasp and discuss them.

It is up to the public to decide.

Acknowledgements

Birger Sørensen helped write the details of our work in PubMed QRDB and Professor Paul R Goddard contributed much of the non-technical aspects, which he covered when writing his book *'PANDEMIC'* (Clinical Press Ltd., June 2020, 2nd edition Sept 2021).

A COVID Bayesian Analysis: How a 'Bookie' Sees the Origin

by Dr Steven Quay

Introduction.

The Covid-19 pandemic has claimed millions of dead, over 200 million confirmed cases[1], and trillions of dollars of economic damage. Although there is universal agreement that a coronavirus identified as Severe Acute Respiratory Syndrome Coronavirus 2 or SARS-CoV-2 (at times also abbreviated CoV-2 henceforth) causes the disease Covid-19, there is no accepted consensus on the true molecular origin of the disease.

The Chinese government, WHO, the mainstream media, and many academic virologists had stated since the very beginning with strong conviction that the coronavirus came from nature, either directly from bats to humans or indirectly from bats through another species. Transmission of a virus from animals to humans is called a zoonosis.

A small but growing number of scientists have considered another hypothesis: that a CoV-2 ancestral bat coronavirus was collected in the wild, genetically manipulated in a laboratory to make it more infectious by training it to attack human cells, and ultimately released, probably by accident, in Wuhan, China. This kind of research is called "Gain-of-Function" by virologists. For most of 2020 this hypothesis was considered a crackpot idea, but in the last few months more media attention has been given to the possibility that the Wuhan Institute of Virology, located near the Wuhan city center, an urban sprawl with a population of over 11 million inhabitants, may have conducted the field specimen collection effort, laboratory genetic manipulation, and subsequent leak. On January 15, 2021, the U.S. Department of State issued a statement requesting the WHO investigation of the origin of Covid-19 include specific assertions related to a laboratory origin of the pandemic.

This initiative will soon be overshadowed by further resounding developments.[(2)]

Given the strong sentiment in the scientific community in favour of a zoonosis and the massive effort undertaken by China to find the natural animal source, one can assume that any evidence in favour of a natural origin, no matter how trivial, had been widely disseminated and known. This provided a potential evidence bias within the scientific community in favour of a natural origin which isn't easily quantifiable but should be kept in mind.

This becomes especially important background if one considers that evidence that supported a laboratory origin had been directly provided by leading Chinese scientists themselves, like Dr. Zheng-Li Shi, head of coronavirus research at the Wuhan Institute of Virology and Gao Fu (George Fu Gao), Director of the Chinese CDC; by the Chinese government, as well as by powerful and vociferous, pro-natural origin scientists, like Dr. Peter Daszak, of the NYC-based NGO *EcoHealth Alliance* and a vocal member of the WHO team that travelled to China for the recent field work on the origin. Later in this chapter I will use the research of these "insiders" to show how evident the lab origin hypothesis already was in the early days of the pandemic.

This chapter is an overview of my original analysis of the evidence for and against a natural zoonosis on the one hand, and on the other I will show how solid and above all shocking the 'lab leak' hypothesis, called a laboratory-acquired infection (LAI), always was. The method I used early on to quantify the likelihood of each hypothesis is called a Bayesian analysis.

In so doing I will also reveal to the non expert reader the unique biological and genetic features of CoV-2 that, if not kept from the international community by both the Chinese authorities and afterwards by the mainstream media, would have alerted policymakers, the health authorities and most importantly the public to the highly aggressive and deadly nature of the novel coronavirus from the very beginning of this calamity.

What is a Bayesian analysis?

This report uses the Bayesian analysis method, a common statistical tool in which the Bayes' theorem, a well-known statistical equation, is used to update the likelihood for a particular hypothesis as more evidence or information becomes available. It is widely used in the sciences and medicine and has begun to be used in the law.

It is also the method used by bookies when they set the odds for betting on sporting events, although probably none of them know they are doing a Bayesian analysis. The three key steps in a Bayesian analysis are:

1. To define a starting point for a prediction about an unknown event or the likelihood of one of two causes for something, whether past or future. In sports betting, it is the future event of who is going to win the baseball game or the World Cup football title. Before the first pitch of the baseball season in the US or the first ball strike on the way to the World Cup, a ranking of teams can be created. It is based on prior performance, injuries, new players or coaches, and many other factors. All of these are expressed in the pre-season rankings that avid fans pour over in the newspaper at breakfast or in the pubs at night.
2. Step two is new information, new data. Once the games start to be played things happen: an unexpected upset by a

motivated but under rated team, an injury of a key player, or a mid-season trade of players. Each of these have an impact on the prior probabilities for who will win.

3. Step three is a new ranking of the probability of who will be standing on the winner's tower at the end of the season based on some simple math and that new information.

You may have never had a passion for mathematics in your life but if you follow sports and the rankings of your favourite team, you have been watching a Bayesian analysis being conducted. And even if you have never heard of Thomas Bayes, the 18th century Scottish Presbyterian minister and part-time statistician who came up with the simple arithmetic that comprises the process, you can appreciate watching it in action.

Before we get into the actual analysis I need, for context, to give a little background on what still to this day, despite the overwhelming evidence to the contrary, is the scientific community's favourite theory of origin, the zoonosis, and how its features compare to a laboratory-acquired infection.

What is a zoonosis?

A viral zoonosis has at least three elements, an animal host, a virus, and the human population. With some viruses there are often two animal hosts. One is a 'reservoir host' where the virus can live for years or even decades in a relatively stable relationship. The reservoir host is never decimated by the virus, and the virus is never burned out by the reservoir host, disappearing completely. For coronaviruses the reservoir host is always one or more bat species. If a coronavirus infects a bat reservoir host but then cannot jump directly into the human population, it may need a second host, an intermediate host.

In this case the virus spends time jumping from its bat host into the intermediate host, 'practicing' adaption through random mutation and Darwinian selection for fitness to reproduce, infect, and transmit in the intermediate host. This process is then repeated between the intermediate host and the human population. Alternatively, the virus can jump directly between the bat reservoir and humans, without the need for an intermediate host.

For two prior human coronavirus epidemics, an intermediate or proximate host was identified. For SARS-CoV-1 in 2003-4 it was the civet-cat while for Middle Eastern Respiratory Syndrome (MERS) in 2012-4 it was the camel. In both of these human epidemics, the intermediate host was identified within four and ten months, respectively, of the first clinically identified human infection. With SARS-CoV-2 we have significantly better techniques and massively more effort expended in finding the intermediate host, but almost two years into this pandemic we are still waiting for any real, convincing, evidence of an intermediate host. For both of these previous epidemics a bat species reservoir host was also identified, but not in the case of SARS-CoV-2.(3)

Among the pantheon of coronavirus scientists in the world the two who are at the apex of the investigation into the origin of Covid-19 are Dr. Peter Daszak, President of the NYC-based *EcoHealth Alliance* and Dr. Zheng-Li Shi, the director of coronavirus research at the Wuhan Institute of Virology, known in the popular Chinese press as *Batwoman*. They have worked together for over a decade and apparently enjoy an evening of karaoke together after a day talking 'virus' at the Wuhan Institute of Virology or a hike to the bat caves.

Based on the genome sequence of CoV-2, Drs. Zheng-Li Shi and Daszak have proposed that the reservoir host for CoV-2 is the intermediate horseshoe bat (Rhinolophus affinis), which is found in Yunnan Province. Yunnan Province is in southern, rural China and about 1900 km from the north central province of Hubei, where the 11 million people of Wuhan live. The intermediate horseshow bat isn't found at all in Hubei province, making a direct bat-to-human transmission improbable.[4] In fact while some virologists had proposed a direct spillover bats-to-humans as the origin of the pandemic, experiments in three independent laboratories threw a spanner in the works of that idea by demonstrating that CoV-2 cannot infect any bat cell culture tested. This provides experimental evidence against a direct bat-to-human transmission. In simpler terms, if SARS-CoV-2 cannot grow in the bats that are supposed to be its reservoir hosts, there is no way that it came from those bats to us humans via a direct spillover in the first place, and at the very least an intermediate host must be found.

So, while the leading US coronavirus expert, Dr. Ralph Baric of The University of North Carolina, suggested in early 2020 that SARS-CoV-2 may have jumped into the human population directly from bats without an intermediate host, this hypothesis seems no longer to be viable. It is also worth noting that the temperatures in Wuhan and the surrounding area are such that from about mid-September, the cold weather sends the bats into their caves to hibernate over the winter. So they actually slept through the start of the pandemic.

For the zoonosis hypothesis to be advanced, it is now necessary to find an intermediate host. In January 2020 a theory was proposed that SARS-CoV-2 arose in the Huanan Seafood Market, a traditional Chinese "wet market" in Wuhan, China, where live animals are butchered and sold for food, thus implying that one of those animals may have been the intermediate host. The market theory was supported by the observation that about 40% of early patients worked or shopped there. This was reminiscent of the wet market sources for civet cats infected with SARS-CoV-1 or the camel markets for the MERS coronavirus in the Middle East. The Chinese authorities closed the market on December 31, 2019 after performing extensive environmental sampling and sanitation.

But by May 2020 Dr. Gao Fu, Director of the Chinese CDC, announced that the market was not the source of CoV-2, as all of the animal specimens tested negative for CoV-2. And while SARS-CoV-1 was found in 100% of local farmed civets when tested, CoV-2 was different: in fact in July 2020 Dr. Zheng-Li Shi reported that extensive testing of farmed animals throughout Hubei Province failed to find SARS-CoV-2 in any animals.

For about six months, the pangolin, a scaly solitary-living anteater, was suspected to be the intermediate host but finally Dr. Daszak reported that CoV-2 was not found in pangolins in the wild or from the (illegal) market trade.[5] Domestic and feral cats also were ruled out as a possible source. A comprehensive computer-based screen of 410 different animals [6] reported the remarkable finding that the best ACE2 receptor matches to CoV-2 were human and other primates (or primate cells in the laboratory), including the favourite laboratory coronavirus host, the VERO monkey cell culture, and that all bat species were the worst host. Not to confuse readers it must be specified that this particular experiment was a computer algorithm study only. As stated previously, when they actually tested CoV-2 in bat cultures it did not grow in any of them.

Furthermore, a typical zoonosis has a number of characteristic properties that can allow identification of a zoonotic infection, even in the absence of identifying an intermediate host. None of these properties are found for Covid-19.

All zoonotic infections have in common the principle that when a virus in nature uses evolution to move from, for example, a bat host to a camel host and then to a human host, it is a hit and miss, slow process. After all, evolution is the result of random genetic changes, mutations, and then enrichment of the ones that are helpful by amplification during reproduction. With both SARS-CoV-1 and MERS, the coronavirus spent months and years jumping from the intermediate host into humans, not having all of the necessary mutations needed to be aggressive, grow, and then spread, but spending enough time in humans to cause an asymptomatic or minor infection and leaving behind a corresponding immune response.

The hallmark evidence of this 'practice' in abortive host jumping is in stored, archived human blood specimens taken from before the epidemic, where one can find evidence of pre-epidemic, usually sub-clinical, community spread in patients from the antibodies to the eventual epidemic virus in that old, stored blood. For SARS-CoV-1 and MERS, about 0.6% of people in the region where the epidemic began showed signs of an infection in archived blood. With CoV-2, this seroconversion, as it is called, has never been observed, including in 540 specimens collected from 'fever clinics' in Wuhan between October 2019 and January 2020, reported by the WHO. Because this is such a potent signal of a zoonosis, and because I believe that China has over 100,000 stored specimens from Wuhan taken in the fall of 2019, the lack of reports of seroconversion, coupled with the silence from China on this evidence, speaks volumes.

Another hallmark of a slow, natural zoonosis can be found in the virus. In SARS-CoV-1 and MERS, the coronavirus spent years in the intermediate host, passing back and forth among populations of hosts, the civets or camels, that were living in close proximity. During this time, they would accumulate a background of genetic mistakes, i.e., mutations; usually about one mistake every two weeks. When the final chip falls, and mutation(s) happens allowing the jump into humans, the virus with that new mutation(s) also jumps around within the intermediate host population.

The consequence of this latter behaviour for a true zoonosis is that the genome sequences found in humans don't all descend from a single jump that came from one single intermediate animal (let's say one single civet-cat) into a single person, but by multiple coincidental jumps from multiple intermediate animals (different civet-cats) thus infecting the very first humans with viruses that are only cousins of each other (having coincidentally come from different civet-cats but still able to infect human beings). In other words, in a true zoonosis, the family tree of virus genome sequences doesn't have a first single patient as the head of the family (that would only occur if the first single patient had been infected by a virus 'trained' in a laboratory). Instead the early human cases from a zoonotic infection have different viruses that are not brothers and sisters of each other but cousins, sometimes very distant cousins. In a true zoonosis the common ancestor that these cousin viruses share may have occurred months or even years before the first human patient.

With CoV-2, there are no cousin viruses. Every one of the 1,594,616 virus genomes sequenced in GISAID, the Germany-based sequence repository, can be traced back to the first human case.

The first patient (a 39-year-old man) with a CoV-2 gene sequence that is the root virus for every case in the world is from a Covid-19 cluster seen at the end of December 2019 at the People's Liberation Army (PLA) Hospital, about 3.4 km from the Wuhan Institute of Virology. The worldwide CoV-2 pandemic has the manmade signature of one genetically pure virus sequence infecting one human, and then with human-to-human spread thereafter. There is just the one and only jump into the human population ever seen. This lack of posterior diversity has been alluded to by Dr. Zheng-Li Shi, by the WHO, and by other prominent virologists; they just never took that critical piece of the evidence to the next proper inference, probably because they were not allowed to do so.

The virus in a true zoonosis also contains the signature record of the gradual changes and adaptions it made in the protein key, the Spike Protein, it uses to unlock human cells and cause infection. As we have already noted true zoonotic epidemics have two discrete phases: a pre-epidemic phase when jumps from animal-to-human occur and cause a single infection but do not support human-to-human spread; and the later epidemic phase, where the ability to support human-to-human spread has been gained. With SARS-CoV-1, the pre-epidemic Spike Protein had fewer than one-third of all the changes it would later develop by the time it achieved human-to-human spread and became an epidemic. With CoV-2 the Spike Protein was almost perfectly adapted to the human lock from the very beginning, using 99.5% of the best amino acids possible.

Since with CoV-2 we have no evidence from stored blood that it was quietly practicing on humans in the community of Wuhan, it is surprising that when it finds its first patient, it has perfected to 99.5% the Spike Protein amino acid sequence, its ability to attack and infect humans. If this adaption couldn't have happened in the community, the only place it could have happened is in a laboratory, by what is called serial passage, a common laboratory process that repeatedly gives the virus a chance to practice on humanized mice or VERO monkey cells.[7]

A related study showing human adaption right from the start of the pandemic looked at which protein manufacturing tools CoV-2 uses (called tRNAs) when it makes copies of itself (CoV-2 does not possess these 'tools' and so it hijacks those of the host cell). It showed the same uncanny adaptation to the human tools with no evidence that the tools from other potential intermediate hosts would be suitable.

This evidence presented already made a strong case in my Bayesian analysis that CoV-2 did not come from nature at the very beginning of the pandemic. But was there already back then affirmative evidence that it could have come from a laboratory?

The answer is yes.

Laboratory Origin Hypothesis

From the beginning of the Covid-19 pandemic two early clues pointed to the two competing theories on how it started, that is zoonosis and lab leak. About half of the first patients had a connection to the Huanan Seafood Market in central Wuhan, China.[8] This market connection was reminiscent of where the prior two coronavirus epidemics had begun.

The other clue was that the Wuhan Institute of Virology (WIV) was near the location of the first cases as well.[9] The proximity of the laboratory to the first cases was reminiscent of the last six SARS lab-leak infections that occurred in China back in 2003-4.[10] After the first SARS epidemic ended in the community, an additional six cases arose separately in laboratory personnel working with or near the SARS virus. These laboratory-acquired infections led to local community outbreaks and even one death.

When one speaks of a laboratory-acquired infection we don't always mean that a virus "leaked" out or "escaped from the lab," as you sometimes hear. What could have happened is that an animal or cells from an animal were infected with the virus for research purposes and then a lab worker accidentally got infected, walked out of the lab while asymptomatic, and then it spread to the community. This is really no different from a classical zoonosis, except instead of the "host" animal being in a market it is from a laboratory and the zoonosis was made possible because it was scientists that adapted the virus to attack humans. From 1986 to 2016 laboratories in Asia averaged one laboratory acquired infection per year by this very process.

In addition to proximity, the WIV is not an ordinary research laboratory but is in fact one of the leading coronavirus research institutions in the world. For almost twenty years its scientists were collecting, transporting, growing in the lab, and doing genetic research on coronaviruses. The lead WIV investigator, as previously mentioned, is Dr. Zheng-Li Shi, known in the Chinese media as *Batwoman* because of her lifetime of coronavirus research. The WIV has been documented to have over 16,000 virus specimens in their possession, for example, but removed a website containing these from public access in September 2019.

Going further in depth in this part on the background stories of the lab-leak of SARS-CoV-2, let's consider the so called Spike Protein of this coronavirus. It gives the coronavirus its name, corona or crown, and is the key to match with the locks found in host cells commonly known as ACE2 receptors. However, as Paolo Barnard has already explained in a previous paragraph that I will summarise here adding new details, before the Spike Protein can inject its genetic material in the host cell, it needs to be cut, to loosen it in preparation for infection. The host cell has the scissors or enzymes that do the cutting. The singular, unique feature of CoV-2 is that it requires a host enzyme called *Furin* to activate it at a spot called the S1/S2 junction. No other coronavirus in the same subgenera has a *Furin Cleavage Site*, as it is called. Also, all other coronaviruses in the group that includes SARS-CoV-2 are not cleaved at the S1/S2 junction, precisely because they lack a *Furin Cleavage Site*, but instead are cleaved at a site downstream from the S1/S2 site, called the S2' site.

This is of course a major problem for the zoonosis theory, but it gets worse.

Since 1992 the virology community has known that the one sure way to make a virus deadlier is to give it a *Furin Cleavage Site* precisely at the S1/S2 junction in the laboratory. At least eleven separate Gain of Function experiments, adding a *Furin Site* at the S1/S2 junction to make a virus more infective, are published in the open literature, including one from Dr. Zheng-Li Shi. This caused a flurry of, mostly, Chinese papers since the pandemic began trying to show a natural *Furin Cleavage Site* in a related virus or to show that *Furin Sites* from distant cousins of CoV-2 might be the source through a process called recombination, where two different viruses infect the same host and then make a mistake in copying their genetic material, and swap sequences.

These convoluted, hypothetical methods each fail to convince, however. It turns out that it is Daszak himself who has shown that the genetic group of coronaviruses that have *Furin Sites* is found in different bat hosts, which live in different regions of China, than the bat hosts expected for SARS-CoV-2's ancestor. This means there are no opportunities for a bat near Wuhan to have had an infection with two viruses, one with a *Furin Cleavage Site* and one without, and for an exchange to have occurred. As noted previously[(11)] Dr. Zheng-Li Shi also did not believe the bats of Hubei province, where Wuhan is located, are capable of being a host for CoV-2-related coronaviruses.

However more clues existed against the zoonotic theory which pointed instead towards the lab-leak hypothesis. Not only are there no *Furin Cleavage Sites* in the Spike Protein of any coronaviruses belonging to the same class as SARS-CoV-2, but the genetic blueprint for making the Spike Protein in this pandemic coronavirus is, yet again, unprecedented.

Here is why: the SARS-CoV-2 genetic blueprint contains so called codons, which are 3-nucleotides "instructions" that will define corresponding amino acids. No need to panic, it's simpler than it sounds. Why is this important? Because amino acids are in turn the building blocks of Spike Proteins. So one could say that these codons are the "instructors" that tell the "building site" where the virus proteins are made what exact bricks (amino acids) to use to build the Spike Protein.

But here comes the surprise: some of the particular "instructors-codons" that are found in the Spikes of SARS-CoV-2 are never found anywhere else in the coronaviruses family's "building sites". And here comes the highly suspicious catch: when scientists in a lab experiment (called Gain-of-Function) purposely intend to manipulate the amino acid structure of a viral Spike Protein in order to make it more aggressive against human cells, they will insert into that Spike precisely those "instructors-codons" that have been found in the nefarious SARS-CoV-2 Spike Protein and not in any other coronavirus.

Why do scientists choose these "instructors-codons" specifically? Because they will build a Spike exquisitely suited to attack us humans, which was the aim of their experiment to begin with. So, let's recap:

- SARS-CoV-2 unnaturally carries these "instructors-codons" and is thus very aggressive on us.
- The pandemic started in Wuhan where a coronavirus Gain-of-Function lab operates.
- Gain-of-Function experiments would use precisely the odd "instructors-codons" found in SARS-CoV-2's Spike to make other viruses better attack human cells.
- SARS-CoV-2 attacks human cells much better than it does animal ones.

At this point the Bayesian 'scientific bookie' could well have rested his case many months ago. It was yet another powerful piece of evidence pointing to Covid-19 having originated from a lab experiment and accidental leak in China, and these were facts known to Dr Zheng-Li Shi since the fall of 2019.

It is telling that when Dr. Zheng-Li Shi introduced CoV-2 to a major peer-reviewed journal for the first time in January 2020 she showed hundreds of gene sequences of this novel virus but stopped just short of showing the *Furin Cleavage Site*, the one she is purported to have introduced, seemingly not wanting to call attention to her handywork. She apparently failed to realize that an accomplished but innocent virologist, finding the first *Furin Site* ever seen in this class of viruses apparently coming from nature, would have featured the presence of the *Furin Site* prominently, and also would have used its presence and her experience with *Furin Sites* in other viruses to predict what it would foretell for the world due to its aggressive nature.

She could have perhaps saved many lives just by telling the world that she saw a *Furin Cleavage Site* in the virus sequence.

It would be left to a French and Canadian team to later identify the *Furin Cleavage Site* in a *peer-reviewed* paper. They would write: *"This Furin-like cleavage site...may provide a **gain-of-function** to the 2019-nCoV for efficient spreading in the human population compared to other lineage b betacoronaviruses."* [Emphasis added.]

Besides noting that SARS-CoV-2 began adjacent to the laboratory with the world's largest collection of coronaviruses as being consistent with a lab origin, finding the signature of two Gain-of-Function coronavirus experiments – the insertion of a *Furin Cleavage Site* and the highly unusual codons – was already a very strong signal of a lab origin that should have alerted the international scientific community to precisely that origin hypothesis for SARS-COV-2.

Dr Zheng-Li Shi has denied the virus came from her lab, but she has created such a record of multiple examples of obfuscation, half-truths, contrived specimens, genetic sequences taken from thin air but published in premier journals and in US NIH databases, etc. that her veracity is deeply damaged. Perhaps her words and actions on December 30, 2019 show the truth. Her very first response when she was told there was an unknown viral outbreak in Wuhan and was ordered to return back quickly from a meeting she was attending in Shanghai was to say, *"Could this have come from our lab?"*[12] *"I wondered if* [the municipal health authority] *got it wrong."* The Wuhan virologist also said *"I had never expected this kind of thing to happen in Wuhan, in central China."*

Her studies had shown that the southern, subtropical provinces of Guangdong, Guangxi and Yunnan have the greatest risk of coronaviruses jumping to humans from animals — particularly bats, a known reservoir. After all, the US equivalent of the distance, climate change, and human population density change between, for example, Yunnan and Wuhan is comparing the Everglades National Park in Florida and New York City, or in Italy it would be the difference between mid Sicily and Milan.

Her other action on December 30 was to alter WIV computer databases of novel coronaviruses used by the world's virologists for research to make it more difficult for outside colleagues to scrutinize which coronaviruses she had been studying in her building. In short, the day she was asked to address the epidemic in Wuhan, she chose to spend time to make unavailable to her fellow scientists of the world part of her decades of coronavirus work. This action has no innocent explanation.

Nonetheless, one must make clear to the readers that transparency is a luxury the WIV scientists like Zheng-Li Shi could not and still cannot afford. That institution works under the strict surveillance of the People's Liberation Army of China and of the China National Health Commission which in turn report to the President of a country that has consistently been in the spotlight of all the major human rights organisations of the world. Dr Zheng-Li Shi was never free to speak out without putting herself and her family at great risk.

However the notion that CoV-2 was a laboratory creation, designed for maximum virulence, that escaped the laboratory accidentally had additional evidence. From President Xi announcing in February 2020 new laws about laboratory security, to abundant evidence that the Wuhan Virology Institute (WIV) was closed in October with few personnel inside, to the top military medical research doctor, General Chen Wei, being placed in charge of the WIV, to many more clues, it is clear an event occurred in Wuhan sometime in late 2019 that was most consistent with a laboratory escape.

Not an extraordinary event after all if one considers that the

Asian region has a two-decade record of about one laboratory-acquired infection per year. After the first SARS-CoV-1 epidemic was ended, SARS-CoV-1 jumped six more times into the human population, all from laboratories, with four escapes in China.

The last smallpox death in the entire world, as Paolo Barnard reminded us in his chapter, was a lab photographer who worked two floors above a research lab in England and contracted it through the ventilation system. The head of that laboratory committed suicide over his anguish for causing her death. His angst was also due to everyone's general panic about a possible pandemic spread of the killer virus, which at that point no one could yet rule out. In fact after his suicide his colleagues had to wait the whole incubation period before ruling out new cases and a new pandemic.

Over and over again. there is a long history and record of laboratory acquired infections that provides the background for considering what happened here.

Bayesian analysis: what its starting point was.

To be clear on where my analysis began, it is good to remind you that the starting probability for the origin of SARS-CoV-2 was set with the zoonotic or natural hypothesis at 98.8% likelihood with the laboratory origin hypothesis set at 1.2%. I personally made the decision to bias the initial state as much as possible towards a zoonotic origin, with the starting point selected from three independent estimates, including one by Daszak and colleagues. Each piece of new evidence for or against each hypothesis was then used to adjust the probabilities. If evidence favoured a natural origin the math adjusted upward the probability of a natural origin, and so on.

Hereafter I propose again, enriched by further crucial evidence, the five incontrovertible key facts that are the pillars of my Bayesian analysis. Collecting our thoughts at this point seems a good idea.

Fact 1. Covid-19 wasn't smouldering in the community before the Wuhan epidemic broke out.

One of the frustrations in stopping epidemics is that, despite the fact they begin with sporadic cases in a community months or even years before the epidemic breaks out, these sporadic cases are only identified in hindsight. After an epidemic has begun and blood tests are developed to identify those who have antibodies or virus in their blood as evidence of an infection, epidemiologists look for clues on how it began by screening archived blood samples in hospitals and clinics near the epicenter of the outbreak. For a natural zoonosis, this testing finds a small but measurable background of "silent" infections in the community that predate the epidemic.

In February 2020, the WHO reported that a retrospective examination of 4500 specimens *"stored at various hospitals in Wuhan, the rest of Hubei Province, and other provinces"* found no evidence of SARS-Cov-2. Given the prevalence of retrospectively tested specimen positivity of between 0.6% and about 4% for SARS and MERS, one would have expected 27 to about 180 positive specimens, not zero.

Another study of 640 specimens tested retrospectively found no positive specimens before the first week of January. Using mathematical modelling they concluded *"the initial pandemic wave in Wuhan likely originated with a single infected case who developed symptoms sometime between October 26 and December 13, 2019."* (13) The probability this was a zoonoses and yet not a single patient with SARS-CoV-2 virus had been found in the local human community before the outbreak, compared to the two previous zoonoses, would have been one in 14,881 or about 0.007%. Of course, the probability that there would be no community infection found before the day when a laboratory-acquired infection (LAI) occurred is 100%. To understand how unlikely this analysis already made a natural zoonosis, a 0.007% probability was the same as being struck by lightning!

These data that Covid-19 began with a single first patient are reminiscent of the previous six laboratory-acquired coronavirus infections and different from the last coronavirus natural zoonoses, SARS and MERS.

Fact 2. The animal host for the Covid-19 coronavirus, or a close relative, has not been found in nature.

Starting in the Huanan Market in Wuhan in December 2019, scientists collected samples on environmental surfaces, in water drains, and from animals for sale. A total of 336 samples from the animals in the market were tested for the SARS-CoV-2 virus by the sensitive PCR testing but none were positive for the virus.(14) This is a critical observation; with SARS or MERS contemporaneous testing always found the markets positive when human cases were appearing. In particular during the 2004 SARS epidemic sixty to ninety per cent of the civet cats found in the traditional markets tested positive for coronavirus infection. Here it is the opposite, in December 2019 human infections are spreading at the same time the market animals are disease free. By May 2020 the Chinese Centers for Disease Control had ruled out the site as the origin of the outbreak.(15)

While a small per cent of the environmental specimens from surfaces were positive for the SARS-CoV-2 virus both the World Health Organization (WHO) and the US Centers for Disease Control and Prevention (CDC) had previously dismissed the idea that disease transmission on packaging could be a serious concern. (16)

With the market ruled out as a potential source, scientists began expanding outward, looking for the elusive virus. At the WHO press conference Dr. Marion Koopmans from the Erasmus Centre in the Netherlands stated: *"Back in 2019 it doesn't look like there was wide circulation of the virus in any animal species in the country."* (17) This statement was based on the significant work that had been done over the previous year. In fact the WHO had claimed that Chinese scientists had taken samples for testing from 11,000 domestic animals and 50,000 wild animals covering over 300 species and from all provinces of China. None of these specimens was positive for the SARS-CoV-2 virus. This was a surprising finding. In a seminal paper in May 2020 on the origin of the virus, leading scientists from the US, UK, and Australia had predicted the animal host would *"probably have a high population density"* because of the unique properties of SARS-CoV-2. This prediction – namely that the virus would not be hosted by a lone and rare animal but by a well known and numerically large species pretty easy to spot – is further support for how unexpected and equally incomprehensible the complete lack of finding the virus in any animal group really was. (18)

Finding no infections out of over 60,000 animals has strong statistical implications about whether it was ever in nature to begin with.

While not finding it in nature, after over a year and a half of intense study on related viruses, the closest genetically related animal virus is still the one disclosed by Dr. Zheng-Li Shi in February 2020, named RATG13. This virus was in the WIV laboratories among specimens that had been collected from bats in 2013 in Yunnan Province, in Southern China about 1900 km from Wuhan. Records from the WIV show this virus was being investigated genetically from 2015 to at least 2018.

Fact. 3 The SARS-CoV-2 coronavirus had little genetic diversity, unlike the prior natural zoonoses.

In the first description of the virus that causes Covid-19 in January 2020, Dr. Zheng-Li Shi wrote, "*(t)he almost identical sequences of this virus in different patients imply a probably recent introduction in humans.*" In a separate publication, an international team of Australian, Chinese, and Scottish scientists wrote, "*(m)any of the genomes from the earliest sampled cases are genetically identical. This occurrence is different to previous viruses and epidemics.*" Everyone agrees the virus looked nearly genetically pure at the beginning of the pandemic. (19)

This is in stark contrast to the first SARS and the MERS(20) viruses: they showed significant genetic diversity right from the beginning. This only makes sense for a natural process. Nature prefers genetic diversity as it assures a robust population of different backgrounds to withstand any environmental change and it is a natural consequence of the way nature and evolution works. In coronavirus zoonoses there is a large population of animal hosts, each with a genetically different virus. When they jump from animals to humans, they bring that background genetic diversity with them.

On the other hand, when mankind intervenes in nature it is almost always with a genetically pure plant or animal. Think of a farm next to a forest. The natural woods contain a diverse population of plants, trees, and animals. On the other hand, the rows of corn in the farmer's field are genetically pure; every corn plant is genetically identical to every other. Think about the Covid-19 vaccines being delivered around the world. Regardless of which pharmaceutical company made the vaccine the FDA and European regulators have assured their people that every dose is genetically identical to every other, no matter where in the world or to whom it is delivered. Since laboratories universally work with genetically pure cultures in their experiments, a hallmark of a laboratory-acquired infection is a virus with little or no genetic diversity, like here with the SARS-CoV-2 virus.

To recap: the absence of pre-pandemic human cases in stored blood and the absence of an animal host, together with the lack of genetic diversity were, and it was evident since the very beginning, what could be called a *singularity*, a first in biological history. One human encounters one animal with a pure virus and gets infected with one genetic version of SARS-CoV-2. This was very consistent with a laboratory origin for the new coronavirus. But these facts do not distinguish between an accident involving a virus that was captured from nature and simply being grown in the laboratory before its inadvertent release and an accident involving a virus upon which human genetic experimentation had been conducted. The remaining two undisputed facts address these competing options.

Fact. 4 The SARS-CoV-2 virus has a genetic trigger that makes it more infectious and that has never been seen before in this group of coronaviruses.

As previously noted, any origin for the SARS-CoV-2 virus must explain the origin of the *Furin Cleavage Site*, which was a surprise finding when scientists closely examined the Spike Protein of this new pandemic coronavirus. Let me stress once more that for a Furin Cleavage Site to spontaneously appear in SARS-CoV-2 one would have needed to have observed a recombination incident in a virus that took place in nature, but in and of itself such a recombination incident is a very difficult, and therefore low probability, event.

On the other hand, in Gain-of-Function laboratories throughout the world *Furin Cleavage Sites* have been purposely inserted into viruses during experiments for almost 30 years, including at the WIV.

Excluding these very direct lab manipulations of viral genomes, the only other example of a virus acquiring a *Furin Cleavage Site* is during serial passage of the virus in a laboratory cell culture, still a human created environment and not nature.[21] Not to put too fine a point on it, this natural origin theory for the *Furin Cleavage Site* is a stretch: to sum up we know that for it to be acquired in the wild a rare recombination event would have to occur, but a recombination-based insertion of a *Furin Site* has never been observed to have occurred in nature. The Bayesian analysis goes on.

Fact 5. The virus was highly adapted for infection of humans from the start.

The CoV-2 virus was highly adapted to infecting humans from the very beginning. This is again different from the first SARS epidemic. To cause a pandemic a virus needs to learn to jump into humans and then perfect human-to-human transmission. The SARS virus in 2003-4 was genetically mapped during the epidemic and there was the slow accumulation of many genetic changes observed in the months after the first jump into humans. The later mutations were part of the human-to-human transmission ability. MERS has, even to this day, not perfected human-to-human transmission, burning out after only a few jumps. There is no current theory that can explain a jump from an animal and that includes the virus being highly adapted to humans as well as human-to-human spread from the beginning, without having first experienced the human environment.

We all recall the apparent delay in China reporting that the SARS-CoV-2 virus was capable of human-to-human transmission. Part of the reason – meaning the innocent part –

for the delay was that virologists were used to natural zoonoses and so had never seen a virus be as efficient at the beginning of an epidemic in human-to-human transmission as the SARS-CoV-2 virus was.

On the other hand, growing this virus in a human-like laboratory setting would provide the perfect environment to allow Darwin's survival of the fittest to take hold and produce a virus highly adapted to humans.

On March 12, 2020, the day the US announced flights were being banned from Europe, Dr. Zheng-Li Shi at the Wuhan Institute of Virology and her US colleagues submitted for publication their experiments growing the SARS-CoV-2 virus in humanized mice. They reported that this virus was lethal to the humanized mice and besides causing a pneumonia, produced an extensive brain infection, as can be seen in actual human patients with Covid-19. Were these very experiments being conducted by Zheng-Li Shi perhaps in 2019 close to the appearance of Covid-19's patient Zero? If the answer is yes, as every factual and molecular piece of evidence suggests, were those experiments the setting within which the lab-leak of SARS-CoV-2 materialised?

The answer can be found in the records of the Wuhan Institute of Virology, records that China has refused to share with the world.

The final mathematics of our scientific 'bookie'

After the input of all of this evidence my Bayesian analysis had already led me to the conclusion that the probability of the pandemic starting as a laboratory-acquired infection was considerably more than 99%. This was a probability that was beyond a reasonable doubt.

For the scientific bookie, the Covid-19 lab origin story is the saga of the 1966 Soccer World Cup, when Pak Doo Ik scored the single goal, leading North Korea to a 1-0 win over Italy. The lab-leak hypothesis, with a starting probability of less than two per cent came back to be the most likely theory of the origin of Covid-19. The evidence, as we have amply demonstrated, was there from the very beginning of this calamity.

References

BARNARD

1. Paul D. Thacker, The Covid-19 Lab Leak Hypothesis: Did the Media Fall Victim to a Misinformation Campaign?, in «BMJ», vol. 374, n. 1656, 2021.
2. Adam O'Neal, A Scientist Who Said No to COVID Groupthink, in «The Wall Street Journal», 11 June 2021.
3. Author's interview with Prof Simon Wain-Hobson13 March 2020, see link: www.youtube.com/watch?v=4SB1e2JGerc&t=274s).
4. Email to the author, 18 March 2020, 10:45 am.
5. Facing up to Long COVID, in «The Lancet», vol. 396, n. 10266, 2020, p. 1861.
6. Video link at www.youtube.com/watch?v=4tN0-KgbvLg&t=7s.
7. Pere Domingo et al., The Four Horsemen of a Viral Apocalypse. The Pathogenesis of SARS-CoV-2 Infection (Covid-19), in «EBioMedicine», vol. 58, 2020, p. 102887.
8. Email to the author of 5 May 2020, 21:37 pm.
9. Wei Feng et al. , Molecular Diagnosis of Covid-19: Challenges and Research Needs , in «Analytical Chemistry», vol. 92, n. 15, 2020, pp. 10196-10209.
10. Email to the author 29 January 2021, 02.28 am.
11. 11 John Noble Wilford, In the Norwegian Permafrost, a New Hunt for the Deadly 1918 Flu Virus , in «The New York Times», 21 August 1998.
12. David A. Relman, To Stop the Next Pandemic, We Need to Unravel the Origins of Covid-19 , in «PNAS», 3 November 2020.
13. Jeffery K. Taubenberger e David M. Morens, 1918 Influenza: The Mother of All Pandemics , in «Emerging Infectious Diseases», vol. 12, n. 1, 2006,pp. 15-22.
14. Jeffery K. Taubenberger et al., Reconstruction of the 1918 Influenza Virus: Unexpected Rewards from the Past, in «mBio», vol. 3, n. 5, 2012, pp.e00201-e00212.
15. Katherine Harmon, What Really Happened in Malta This September When Contagious Bird Flu Was First Announced? , in «Scientific American», 30 December 2011.

16. Simon Wain-Hobson, An Avian H7N1 Gain-of-Function Experiment of Great Concern , in «mBio», vol. 5, n. 5, 2014, pp. e01882-01814.
17. Ian Sample, Scientists Condemn «Crazy, Dangerous» Creation of Deadly Airborne Flu Virus , in «The Guardian», 11 June 2014.
18. Tokiko Watanabe et al., Circulating Avian Influenza Viruses Closely Related to the 1918 Virus Have Pandemic Potential, in «Cell Host & Microbe», vol. 15, n. 6, 2014, pp. 692-705.
19. S. Wain-Hobson, An Avian H7N1 Gain-of-Function Experiment of Great Concern , cit.
20. Simon Wain-Hobson, H5N1 Viral-Engineering Dangers Will Not Go Away, in «Nature», vol. 495, n. 7442, 2013, p. 411.
21. Email to the author, 8 March 2020, 09:31 am.
22. Marc Lipsitch e Alison P. Galvani, Ethical Alternatives to Experiments with Novel Potential Pandemic Pathogens, in «Plos Medicine», vol. 11, n. 5, 2014, p. e1001646.
23. Peter Daszak, Understanding the Risk of Bat Coronavirus Emergence, Project Number 1R01AI110964-01, National Institute of Allergy and Infectious Diseases, USA, 27 May 2014.
24. Vineet D. Menachery et al. , A SARS-Like Cluster of Circulating Bat Coronaviruses Shows Potential for Human Emergence , in «Nature Medicine», vol. 21, n. 12, 2015, pp. 1508-1513.
25. Zheng-Li Shi et al., Bat Severe Acute Respiratory Syndrome-Like Coronavirus WIV1 Encodes an Extra Accessory Protein, ORFX, Involved in Modulation of the Host Immune Response, in «Journal of Virology», vol. 90, n. 14, 2016, pp. 6573-6582 and Ben Hu et al., Discovery of a Rich Gene Pool of Bat SARS-Related Coronaviruses Provides New Insights into the Origin of SARS Coronavirus, in «Plos Pathogens», 30 November 2017.
26. Peter Daszak, Understanding the Risk of Bat Coronavirus Emergence, Project Number 2R01AI110964-06, National Institute of Allergy and Infectious Diseases, USA, 24 July 2019.
27. Z.-L. Shi et al., Bat Severe Acute Respiratory Syndrome-Like Coronavirus WIV1, cit.
28. John Xie, Chinese Lab with Checkered Safety Record Draws Scrutiny over Covid-19, in «VoA News», 21 April 2020.

29. Milton Leitenberg, Did the SARS-CoV-2 Virus Arise from a Bat Coronavirus Research Program in a Chinese Laboratory? Very Possibly , in «Bulletin of the Atomic Scientists», 4 June 2020.
30. William Burr e Thomas S. Blanton, The Submarines of October. US and Soviet Naval Encounters During the Cuban Missile Crisis , National Security Archive, n. 75, 2002.
31. Martin E. Hellman e Vinton G. Cerf, An Existential Discussion: What Is the Probability of Nuclear War?, in «Bulletin of the Atomic Scientists», 18 March 2021.
32. Monica Rimmer, How Smallpox Claimed Its Final Victim, in «BBC News», 10 August 2018.
33. Joel O. Wertheim, The Re-Emergence of H1N1 Influenza Virus in 1977: A Cautionary Tale for Estimating Divergence Times Using Biologically Unrealistic Sampling Dates , in «Plos one», 17 June 2010.
34. Belgian Biosafety Server Report on SARS in Singapore, 2003.
35. Taiwan's New SARS Case Raises Questions About Sloppy Procedures, in «USA Today», 17 December 2003.
36. World Health Organization, China Reports additional SARS Cases, 23 April 2004.
37. Martin Furmanski, Threatened Pandemics and Laboratory Escapes: Self- Fulfilling Prophecies, in «Bulletin of the Atomic Scientists», 31 March 2014.
38. Alison Young, CDC 2008 Autoclave Potential Exposure Incident, in «USA Today», 31 January 2008.
39. Alison Young, Newly Disclosed CDC Biolab Failures «Like a Screenplay for a Disaster Movie» , in «USA Today», 2 June 2016.
40. Alison Young, CDC Email 31 May 2011 Re Tech Leaving Lab Without Showering , in «USA Today», 31 May 2011.
41. Donald G. McNeil Jr., CDC Closes Anthrax and Flu Labs After Accidents , in «The New York Times», 11 July 2014.
42. Thomas P. van Boeckel et al., The Nosoi Commute: A Spatial Perspective on the Rise of BSL-4 Laboratories in Cities, Cornell Univ, arXiv.org, 2013.
43. Email to the author 18 May 2020, 17.00 pm.
44. Angela L. Rasmussen, On the Origins of SARS-CoV-2 , in

«Nature Medicine», vol. 27, n. 9, 2021.
45. Twitter post by Richard Ebright: twitter.com/r_h_ebright/status /1261660326082367489?lang=en.
46. Zoom Corona Round Table. SARS-CoV-2 and Covid-19: Science in the Spotlight, 6 October 2020: ensser.org/events/2020/zoom-corona-round-table-SARS-CoV-2-and-Covid-19-science-in-the-spotlight/.
47. Cara E. Brook et al., Accelerated Viral Dynamics in Bat Cell Lines, with Implications for Zoonotic Emergence, in «eLife», vol. 9, 2020.
48. For in depth see batonehealth.org.
49. Series of emails to the author, from17 February 2020, 21:56 pm
50. Michael Boots et al. , Synergistic China-US Ecological Research Is Essential for Global Emerging Infectious Disease Preparedness , in «EcoHealth», vol.17, 2020, pp. 160-173.
51. Virginie Courtier, Media Note Re Covid-19 Origins Report Pdf, PhD, Institut Jacques Monod, France, 2021.
52. P. Daszak, Understanding the Risk of Bat Coronavirus Emergence , Project Number 1R01AI110964-01, cit.; P. Daszak, Understanding the Risk of Bat Coronavirus Emergence , Project Number 2R01AI110964-06, cit.; Fred Guterl, Dr. Fauci Backed Controversial Wuhan Lab with US Dollars for Risky Coronavirus Research , in «Newsweek», 28 April 2020.
53. U.S. Government Gain-of-Function Deliberative Process and Research Funding Pause on Selected Gain-of-Function Research Involving Influenza, MERS, and SARS Viruses , 17 October 2014.
54. Is China the World's Top Trader? , CSIS, China Power Project, 2020.
55. Eric Palmer, How Much Does Us Rely on China for Drugs? FDA Simply Doesn't Know, in «FiercePharma», 12 March 2020.
56. Kangpeng Xiao et al. , Isolation of SARS-CoV-2-Related Coronavirus from Malayan Pangolins , in «Nature», vol. 583, 2020, pp. 286-289; Ping Liu et al. , Are Pangolins the Intermediate Host of the 2019 Novel Coronavirus (SARS-CoV-2)? , in «Plos Pathogens», vol. 17, n. 6, 2020, p. e1009664.
57. Email to the author 10 November 2020, 19:38 pm.

58. Sainath Suryanarayanan, EcoHealth Alliance Orchestrated Key Scientists' Statement on «Natural Origin» of SARS-CoV-2 , in «Independent Science News», 19 November 2020.
59. Charles Calisher et al., Statement in Support of the Scientists, Public Health Professionals, and Medical Professionals of China Combatting Covid-19, in «The Lancet», vol. 395, n. 10226, 2020, pp. e42-e43.
60. S. Suryanarayanan, EcoHealth Alliance Orchestrated Key Scientists' Statement on «natural origin» of SARS-CoV-2, cit.
61. Rodolphe de Maistre e Gilles Demaneuf, Selling Science. Scientific Journals and Challenges in China, 14 February 2020: rdemaistre.medium.com.
62. Email by Professor Nikolai Petrovsky to Paolo Barnard 6 April 2021, 06:50 am.
63. Jeremy Page e Drew Hinshaw, China Refuses to Give WHO Raw Data on Early Covid-19 Cases, in «The Wall Street Journal», 12 February 2021.
64. V. Courtier, Media Note Re Covid-19 Origins Report Pdf , cit.
65. Jorge Casesmeiro Roger, An Interview with Richard Ebright: The WHO Investigation Members Were «Participants in Disinformation», in «Independent Science News», 24 March 2021.
66. After Wuhan Mission on Pandemic Origins, WHO Team Dismisses Lab Leak Theory, in «The Washington Post», 9 February 2021.
67. World Health Organization, WHO-Convened Global Study of the Origins of SARS-CoV-2: Terms of References for the China Part, 31 July 2020.
68. V. Courtier, Media Note Re Covid-19 Origins Report Pdf, cit.; Calls for Further Inquiries into Coronavirus Origins, in «The New York Times», 7 April 2021.
69. Nick Schifrin, How Virus Research Has Become a Point of Tension for the US and China , Pbs.org, 22 March 2020.
70. M. Leitenberg, Did the SARS-CoV-2 Virus Arise from a Bat Coronavirus Research Program in a Chinese Laboratory? , cit.; Aylin Woodward, At Least 5 People in China Have Disappeared,

Gotten Arrested, or Been Silenced After Speaking out About the Coronavirus. Here's What We Know About Them, in «Business Insider», 20 February 2020.
71. James T. Areddy, China Rules out Animal Market and Lab as Coronavirus Origin, in «The Wall Street Journal», 26 May 2020.
72. Shing Hei Zhan et al., SARS-CoV-2 Is Well Adapted for Humans. What Does This Mean for Re-Emergence?, bioRxiv, 2 May 2020.
73. P. Daszak, Understanding the Risk of Bat Coronavirus Emergence, Project Number 2R01AI110964-06, cit.
74. Yuri Deigin et al., Should We Discount the Laboratory Origin of Covid-19?, in «Environmental Chemistry Letters», 25 March 2021.
75. Steven Carl Quay, A Bayesian Analysis Concludes Beyond a Reasonable Doubt That SARS-CoV-2 Is Not a Natural Zoonosis but Instead Is Laboratory Derived, Zenodo, 2021.
76. Twitter post by Alina Chan, 30 May 2020: twitter.com/ayjchan/status/1266805310313967617?lang=en.
77. Markus Hoffmann et al. , A Multibasic Cleavage Site in the Spike Protein of SARS-CoV-2 Is Essential for Infection of Human Lung Cells , in «Molecular Cell», vol. 78, n. 4, 2020, pp. 779-784.
78. Jian Shang et al., Cell Entry Mechanisms of SARS-CoV-2, in «PNAS», vol. 117, n. 21, 2020, pp. 11727-11734.
79. Y. Deigin et al. , Should We Discount the Laboratory Origin of Covid-19? , cit.
80. Peng Zhou et al., A Pneumonia Outbreak Associated with a New Coronavirus of Probable Bat Origin, in «Nature», vol. 579, 2020, pp. 270-273.
81. V. Courtier, Media Note Re Covid-19 Origins Report Pdf, cit.
82. Aksel Fridstrøm, The Evidence Which Suggests That This Is No Naturally Evolved Virus, in «Minervanett», 13 July 2020.
83. Jonathan Matthews, Why Are the Lab Escape Denialists Telling Such Brazen Lies?, in «GM Watch», 17 June 2020.
84. Expert Reaction: Did Covid-19 Come from a Lab in Wuhan?, in «Scimex», 17 April 2020.
85. Jon Cohen, Trump «Owes Us an Apology». Chinese Scientist at the Center of Covid-19 Origin Theories Speaks out , in «Science»,

24 July 2020.
86. P. Zhou et al. , A Pneumonia Outbreak Associated with a New Coronavirus of Probable Bat Origin , cit.
87. US Department of State, Fact Sheet: Activity at the Wuhan Institute of Virology, 15 January 2021.
88. David Asher e Miles Yu, Transcript: The Origins of Covid-19: Policy Implications and Lessons for the Future, Hudson Institute, 17 March 2021.
89. Dany Shoham, The Roots of the Covid-19 Pandemic , BESA - The Begin-Sadat Center for Strategic Studies, 14 December 2020; Kirsty Needham, Exclusive: China Gene Firm Providing Worldwide COVID Tests Worked with Chinese Military , Reuters, 30 January 2021.

DALGLEISH

1. Yuxuan Hou et al., Angiotensin-Converting Enzyme 2 (ACE2) Proteins of Different Bat Species Confer Variable Susceptibility to SARS-CoV Entry, in «Archives of Virology», vol. 155, n. 10, 2010, pp. 1563-1569.
2. Wuze Ren et al. , Difference in Receptor Usage Between Severe Acute Respiratory Syndrome (SARS) Coronavirus and SARS-Like Coronavirus of Bat Origin , in «Journal of Virology», vol. 82, n. 4, 2008, pp. 1899-1907.
3. Peng Zhou et al. , Fatal Swine Acute Diarrhoea Syndrome Caused by an HKU2-Related Coronavirus of Bat Origin , in «Nature», vol. 556, 2018, pp. 255-258.
4. Alan D. Workman et al. , The Role of Bitter and Sweet Taste Receptors in Upper Airway Immunity , in «Current Allergy and Asthma Reports», vol. 15, n. 12, 2015, p. 72.
5. Birger Sørensen et al., Biovacc-19: A Candidate Vaccine for Covid-19 (SARS-CoV-2) Developed from Analysis of Its General Method of Action for Infectivity, in «QRB Discovery», vol. 1, n. 6, 2020, pp. 1-11.
6. K. Andersen et al. , The Proximal Origin of SARS-CoV-2 , cit.
7. V.D. Menachery et al., A SARS-Like Cluster of Circulating Bat Coronaviruses Shows Potential for Human Emergence, cit.

QUAY

1. Covid-19 Daily Statistics, see link: worldometers.info/coronavirus.
2. US Department of State, Ensuring a Transparent, Thorough Investigation of Covid-19's Origin, 15 January 2021.
3. I am distinguishing here the difference between SARS-CoV-2 being related to a bat coronavirus, RaTG13 (with 3.8% or 1100 nucleotide (nt) differences between them) and with decades of evolution between them and the closeness of the immediate intermediate host virus which usually within <10, and at most <100 nt different.
4. "We have done bat virus surveillance in Hubei Province for many years but have not found that bats in Wuhan or even the wider Hubei Province carry any coronaviruses that are closely related to SARS-CoV-2. I don't think the spillover from bats to humans occurred in Wuhan or in Hubei Province," said Dr. Shi. Science, July 2020
5. Jimmy Lee et al., No Evidence of Coronaviruses or Other Potentially Zoonotic Viruses in Sunda Pangolins (Manis Javanica) Entering the Wildlife Trade Via Malaysia, in «EcoHealth», vol. 17, n. 3, 2020, pp. 406-418.
6. 6 Joana Damas et al., Broad Host Range of SARS-CoV-2 Predicted by Comparative and Structural Analysis of ACE2 in Vertebrates, in «PNAS», vol. 117, n. 36, 2020, pp. 22311-22322.
7. It is noteworthy that the furin cleavage site is actually unstable in passage in VERO cells and is often deleted within a few passages. A laboratory origin theory needs to account for this observation. On the other hand, mutations in the furin site among the human CoV-2 genomes are exceedingly rare.
8. Qun Li et al. , Early Transmission Dynamics in Wuhan, China, of Novel Coronavirus-Infected Pneumonia , in «The New England Journal of Medicine», vol. 382, n. 13, 2020, pp. 1199-1207.
9. Here are examples of patients 3.4 and 9.1 km from the WIV.
10. Ai Ee Ling, Editorial on Laboratory-Acquired Incidents in Taipei, Taiwan and Singapore Following the Outbreak of SARS Coronavirus , in «Applied Biosafety», vol. 12, n. 1, 2007, p. 17.

11. B. Coutard, C. Valle, X. de Lamballerie, B. Canard, N.G. Seidah, E. Decroly. The spike glycoprotein of the new coronavirus 2019-nCoV contains a furin-like cleavage site absent in CoV of the same clade. Antiviral Research, Volume 176, 2020, https://doi.org/10.1016/j.antiviral.2020.104742
12. Special Report: The Coronavirus Pandemic, in «Scientific American», 1° June 2020.https://www.scientificamerican.com/index.cfm/_api/render/file/?method=inline&-fileID=E1FDF8DE-9E22-4CE5-AD8B2E4682F52A86
13. Zhanwei Du et al. , Using the Covid-19 to Influenza Ratio to Estimate Early Pandemic Spread in Wuhan, China and Seattle, US , in «EClinical-Medicine», vol. 26, 2020, p. 100479; Wen-Hua Kong et al. , SARS-CoV-2 Detection in Patients with Influenza-Like Illness , in «Nature Microbiology», vol. 5, n. 5, 2020, pp. 675-678.
14. World Health Organization, WHO-Convened Global Study of the Origins of SARS-CoV-2, 5 November 2020.
15. Aylin Woodward, The Chinese CDC Now Says the Coronavirus Didn't Jump to People at the Wuhan Wet Market. Instead, It Was the Site of a Superspreader Event, in «Business Insider», 29 May 2020.
16. Amanda Heidt, Coronavirus Found on Food Packaging, but Likely of Little Concern, in «The Scientist», 13 agosto 2020; International Commission on Microbiological Specifications for Foods, ICMSF Opinion on SARS-CoV-2 and Its Relationship to Food Safety, 3 September 2020.
17. World Health Organization, Covid-19 Virtual Press Conference Transcript, 9 febbraio 2021 (da 1:00 a 1:06).
18. Kristian Andersen et al., The Proximal Origin of SARS-CoV-2, in «Nature Medicine», vol. 26, n. 4, 2020, pp. 450-452.
19. Jason W. Rausch et al., Low Genetic Diversity May Be an Achilles Heel of SARS-CoV-2, in «PNAS», vol. 117, n. 40, 2020, pp. 24614-24616.
20. Sayed S. Sohrab ed Ezam I. Azhar, Genetic Diversity of MERS-CoV Spike Protein Gene in Saudi Arabia, in «Journal of Infection and Public Health», vol. 13, n. 5, 2020, pp. 709-717.
21. K. Andersen et al., The Proximal Origin of SARS-CoV-2, cit.

About the Authors

Paolo Barnard, 63, is an Italian senior reporter who co-founded the investigative journalism, award winning, TV show *Report* for State broadcaster RAI where he featured for decades specializing in international current affairs. He was frequently hosted as a columnist on a range of national private TV networks, most notably for La7 in Milan, and on radio shows. He contributed to all major Italian national newpapers inclunding *Il Corriere della Sera* and *La Stampa*, and as an essayist for *Il Sole 24 Ore* (Golem). He has authored several best selling books for Rizzoli, BUR (Milan) and others. He retired from active reporting in 2019.

Dr. Steven Quay, MD, PhD is both a scientist and physician. He was a resident at the Harvard-MGH Hospital, a postdoctoral scientist with Nobel Laureate Gobind Khorana at MIT, and was on the faculty of Stanford University School of Medicine. He has presented evidence to the US State Department, the Department of Homeland Security, and testified before the Congress on the Origin of the Covid-19 pandemic by virtue of his pioneering work on the inconsistencies of the zoonotic hypothesis. He has 360+ published contributions to medicine and has been cited over 10,500 times, placing him in the top 1% of scientists. He holds 87 US patents in 22 fields of medicine and has invented seven FDA-approved pharmaceuticals which have been prescribed to over 80 million people. He is the CEO of Atossa Therapeutics Inc., a clinical-stage biopharmaceutical company developing novel therapeutics for oncology and infectious diseases.

Professor Angus Dalgleish is Professor of Oncology at St Georges Hospital, London and former Visiting Professor at the Institute of Cancer Research in London and also at the Earle Childes Research Institute in Portland, Oregon, USA, and the University of Stellenbosch, South Africa. He was the co-discoverer of the CD4 receptor as the major cellular receptor for HIV and produced the first report of a link between Slim Disease in Africa and HIV infection. Professor Dalgleish pioneered the re-purposing of thalidomide and with support from Celgene helped to develop Lenalidomide which has become one of the largest selling Oncology drugs in the world. In respect of this he received the Joshua Lederberg prize from Celgene in 2011. He has worked closely with Dr Birger Sørensen of Norway in producing vaccines against AIDS and against Severe Acute Respiratory Syndrome Coronavirus 2 (SARS-CoV-2, the virus that has caused the Covid-19 pandemic). He is a Fellow of many learned societies including the Academy of Medical Sciences, the Royal College of Physicians, the Royal College of Pathologists and the Royal Australasian College of Physicians.